NATURE/**SCIENCE ANNUAL**

TIME
LIFE
BOOKS
®

THE TIME-LIFE LIBRARY OF BOATING

HUMAN BEHAVIOR

THE ART OF SEWING

THE OLD WEST

THE EMERGENCE OF MAN

THE AMERICAN WILDERNESS

THE TIME-LIFE ENCYCLOPEDIA OF GARDENING

LIFE LIBRARY OF PHOTOGRAPHY

THIS FABULOUS CENTURY

FOODS OF THE WORLD

TIME-LIFE LIBRARY OF AMERICA

TIME-LIFE LIBRARY OF ART

GREAT AGES OF MAN

LIFE SCIENCE LIBRARY

THE LIFE HISTORY OF THE UNITED STATES

TIME READING PROGRAM

LIFE NATURE LIBRARY

LIFE WORLD LIBRARY

FAMILY LIBRARY:

    HOW THINGS WORK IN YOUR HOME

    THE TIME-LIFE BOOK OF THE FAMILY CAR

    THE TIME-LIFE FAMILY LEGAL GUIDE

    THE TIME-LIFE BOOK OF FAMILY FINANCE

1976 NATURE/SCIENCE ANNUAL

EDITION

TIME-LIFE BOOKS, NEW YORK

TIME-LIFE BOOKS

FOUNDER: Henry R. Luce 1898-1967

Editor-in-Chief: Hedley Donovan
Chairman of the Board: Andrew Heiskell
President: James R. Shepley

Vice Chairman: Roy E. Larsen

MANAGING EDITOR: Jerry Korn
Assistant Managing Editors: Ezra Bowen,
David Maness, Martin Mann, A. B. C. Whipple
Planning Director: Oliver E. Allen
Art Director: Sheldon Cotler
Chief of Research: Beatrice T. Dobie
Director of Photography: Melvin L. Scott
Senior Text Editors: Diana Hirsh, William Frankel
Assistant Planning Director: Carlotta Kerwin
Assistant Art Director: Arnold C. Holeywell
Assistant Chief of Research: Myra Mangan

PUBLISHER: Joan D. Manley
General Manager: John D. McSweeney
Business Manager: John Steven Maxwell
Sales Director: Carl G. Jaeger
Promotion Director: Paul R. Stewart
Public Relations Director: Nicholas Benton

NATURE/SCIENCE ANNUAL

EDITOR: Jane D. Alexander
Text Editor: John Man
Designer: Edward Frank
Staff Writers: Simone D. Gossner, James A. Randall
Chief Researcher: Catherine Ireys
Researchers: Diane Asselin, Millie Swanson,
Gretchen Wessels
Editorial Assistant: Karen Z. Barnard

EDITORIAL PRODUCTION

Production Editor: Douglas B. Graham
Assistant Production Editors:
Gennaro C. Esposito, Feliciano Madrid
Quality Director: Robert L. Young
Assistant Quality Director: James J. Cox
Associate: Serafino J. Cambareri
Copy Staff: Eleanore W. Karsten (chief),
Mary Ellen Slate, Charles Blackwell,
Elaine Pearlmutter, Florence Keith, Pearl Sverdlin
Picture Department: Dolores A. Littles,
Carolyn Turman
Traffic: Carmen McLellan

ON THE COVER

A red fox peers alertly from the snowy shelter of stacked culvert pipe, ready for installation along the service road that parallels Alaska's 800-mile-long pipeline. The fox, like dozens of other wild animal species—many rare in the Lower 48 —seems to be adapting well to man's most ambitious engineering feat since the building of the Panama Canal.

Valuable assistance in preparing this book was provided by the following departments and individuals of Time Inc.: Editorial Production, Norman Airey; Library, Benjamin Lightman; Picture Collection, Doris O'Neil; Photographic Laboratory, George Karas; TIME-LIFE News Service, Murray J. Gart; Correspondents Maria Vincenza Aloisi and Josephine du Brusle (Paris), Margot Hapgood and Dorothy Bacon (London), Elisabeth Kraemer (Bonn), Ann Natanson (Rome), Bernard Diederich (Mexico City), John Dunn (Melbourne), Elaine Farbenbloom and Leslie Hazelton (Jerusalem), Anne Callahan, Barry Hager and Jerry Hannifin (Washington D.C.), Verna Hopkins and Ed Ogle (Vancouver), Harold P. Hostetler (Hawaii), Anton Koene and Sue Masterman (Rijswijk, Netherlands), Robert L. Kroon (Geneva), Mark Morrison (Houston), Franz Spelman (Munich), Barry Wilson (Saskatchewan), Sue Wymelenberg (Boston).

Beginning with this edition, *Nature/Science Annual* will appear in autumn instead of at the end of the calendar year, as it has in the past. This change in publication date is being made so that the coverage can correspond more closely to the working year observed by most scientists, that is, the June-to-June academic year. While all subsequent volumes will cover a full 12 months, the *1976 Annual* covers only nine. This change involves a temporary departure from the normal format: There is no report of the Nobel prizes, which fall at the beginning of next year's cycle and will appear in the *1977 Annual*.

Contents

Big Thicket's Big Ecology

Sprawling over 3.5 million acres of southeast Texas is some of the most unusual real estate in the United States: swampy woodland, called by locals Big Thicket and by conservationists "the biological crossroads of North America." Hyperbole aside, Big Thicket is certainly big ecology; flora and fauna found in virtually every part of the nation flourish together in its green fastness. Scientists speculate that the Thicket's diversity results primarily from successive ice ages millions of years ago, which brought Northern and Eastern life forms into its territory.

Efforts to conserve this unmatched national laboratory were long frustrated by the fact that it was situated in an essential timber region. Finally, in 1974, the timber companies (including a subsidiary of Time Inc.) and the federal government worked out an unusual plan. They would set aside 84,500 acres of Big Thicket as the Big Thicket National Preserve, not as a single massive block of land but as separate, interconnected parcels—eight biologically rich areas that conserve a unique natural heritage for the future.

Linked sections of Big Thicket National Preserve (green areas) sprawl between Texas' Trinity and Sabine Rivers.

Fog-filtered sunlight makes strands of moss glow like jewels in a section that resembles Florida's Everglades.

Baygalls: Miniswamps of the Tropics

Although it looks like a chunk of South American rain forest, the swamp at right is actually part of the Big Thicket National Preserve. Such swamps, located in various parts of the preserve, are called baygalls after their most numerous trees —sweet bays and gallberries. Baygalls are not just ordinary swamps, however. They are miniswamps that are formed when streams change their paths, leaving behind ponds whose bottoms slowly become filled with rich organic matter that sifts down from nearby vegetation.

Rainfalls of up to 60 inches a year keep the baygalls' rich soils saturated, supporting such botanical luxuriance that the swamps sprout impenetrable forests. Their green walls of briars and shrubs tangled amidst barricades of barrel-trunked trees harbor hundreds of species of tropical animals, including herons, giant tree frogs, poisonous cottonmouth moccasins, and alligators. But most of all, the baygalls are seen by conservationists as biological oases, where the proximity of different plants has caused species to interbreed and produce offspring so new that they have yet to be named or classified.

Bulbous trunks of sweet bay, black gum and cypress trees thrust through floating formations of aquatic plants called water shields in a baygall swamp located in the eastern Thicket.

A brightly colored lichen, ruffled like a flower, grows from a damp log in a baygall, where ever-present moisture stimulates the spread of such fungi.

Flashing a menacingly toothy smile, an alligator cools off in a Big Thicket swamp. Once near extinction in the United States, these amphibians are making a comeback in the densely forested enclaves of baygall swamps.

Beauty and Death on a Green Savannah

That the Big Thicket is a region of botanical contrasts is graphically illustrated by the plants shown here. Growing side by side on Thicket grasslands called savannahs are numerous species of ferns, rare orchids and four of North America's five carnivorous plants.

The carnivorous plants are the savannahs' main attraction, for they are the most bizarre of the plant groups in this part of the preserve. Sundew plants *(top right)* use brilliant red filaments with viscous, sweet-smelling juices to invite insects, which stick to the filaments as if they were flypaper. Then the filaments curl about the hapless prey and begin to absorb their juices. Aptly named pitcher plants *(bottom right)* look innocent enough, but their oddly shaped leaves produce a liquid that attracts insects, which then fall into the plant opening and are dissolved by powerful chemicals in the liquid.

An odd couple in the savannah are a rare, highly developed fringe orchid in the foreground and behind it, a cinnamon fern, which is one of the oldest and most primitive of plants.

Looking more like some fleshy creature than a flower, the grass-pink orchid is extremely rare because the sandy wet soil it requires is found in few places outside the Thicket.

Clusters of sundew blossoms (left) glitter with a fluid that attracts and then catches insects. Above, a closeup of one blossom shows an ant captured by the sticky filaments of the sundew.

A shriveled brown pitcher plant is flanked by healthy pitcher plants, one of which displays the curiously shaped bloom of this carnivore, whose slanted bristles trap insects inside.

Southeastern Curiosities in the Southwest

Only 50 miles from Houston, this heavily forested tract of the Big Thicket is home to strangely out-of-place animals. The flying squirrel and the green snake are two of many creatures more usually found in the Southeast than the Southwest.

Scientists believe that eons ago the Big Thicket had cool weather that lured Eastern animals into the area, where they remained after the weather grew warmer. This adaptive cycle may also explain the presence of plants like the giant cypress, which is found mostly in Florida. Seeds of such trees may have been carried by wind or birds during the cooler period, and thrived, providing habitats for animals like the flying squirrel.

The huge light-gathering eyes of a nocturnal flying squirrel glow eerily as the animal perches on a limb. The squirrel cannot actually fly, but glides from tree limbs to the ground aided by thin membranes between its legs.

One of the Big Thicket's sinuous green snakes twines around a branch in a never-ending search for the next meal. Its green color acts as camouflage, shielding it from the insects and small animals that are its favorite foods.

A Southeastern giant, this massive cypress tree dwarfs mossy cypress knees. The cone-shaped root extensions that poke aboveground act like snorkels to allow the roots growing in wet-soil regions to breathe.

In Texas, a Bit of Appalachia

The scenes shown here might easily be found in New York State, or even as far north as Ontario. Actually they are another testament to the Big Thicket's biological diversity. Scattered about its northeastern portion, near streams where soil is cool and well drained, are Northern trees like the beech, and flowers like the iris, which have somehow found their way south and west from North Carolina. In these Big Thicket oases also are immigrants such as the Eastern tiger swallowtail butterfly and perhaps even a few elusive survivors of the ivory-billed woodpecker, a species thought extinct until its distinctive cry was heard echoing through the tall beeches.

◄ *In the northeast region of the Big Thicket near Village Creek, long branches of a massive and ancient beech tree hang toward the underbrush like spindly crooked arms.*

The stamens of this purple pleatleaf iris, common in North Carolina, provide a target for pollinating insects.

A swallowtail butterfly floats down on a wild azalea, a plant that is usually found in the Appalachian region.

The fly amanita is a poisonous mushroom that is quickly identified by the insect-like scabs on its top.

Flowers adorn the branches of a dogwood, a tree mainly found on the East Coast that thrives in the Big Thicket.

Pines and birches poke through the early morning mist that swathes the Big Thicket. The strip between the trees is a logging trail—one of many roads, railways and cultivated fields that mingle with the vast and lonely timberlands.

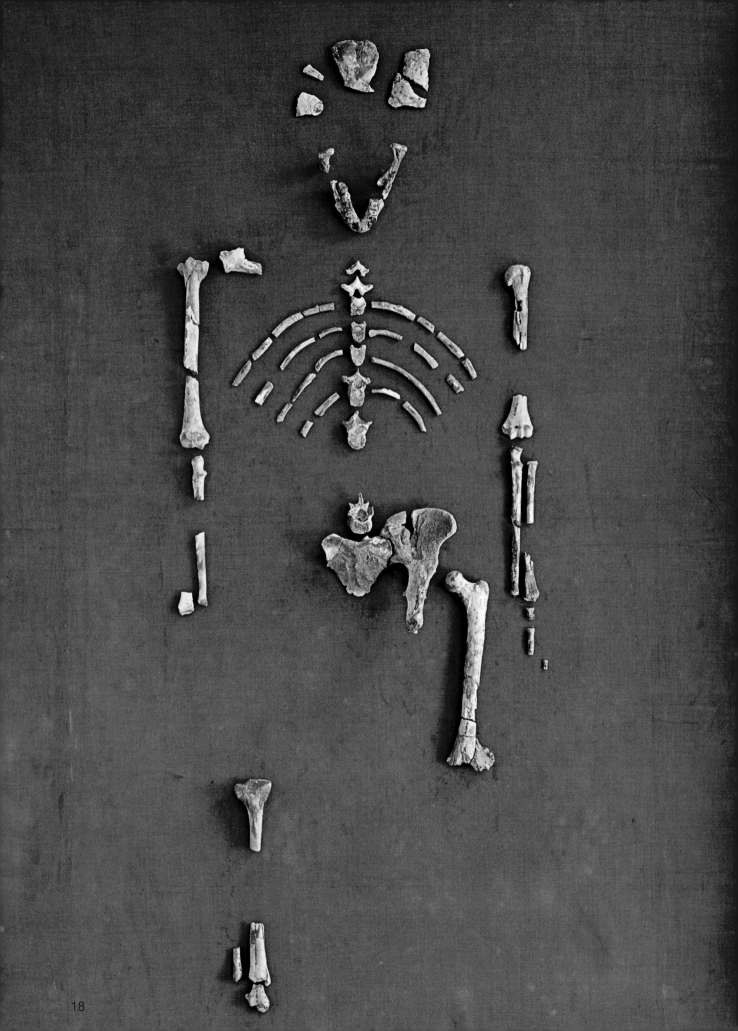

Three-Million-Year-Old Lucy

OLDEST HUMAN-LIKE SKELETON IS FOUND, 40% COMPLETE

by Maitland A. Edey

At about noon one November day in 1974 Don Johanson, a young American paleoanthropologist working in a remote part of Ethiopia, began thinking about lunch. He was far from comfortable. He had been trudging about for some time in the blazing sun, helping a geologist with some mapping. Now, at midday, the temperature in the semidesert area in which he was working had soared to well over 100 degrees. The area itself, north and east of Addis Ababa, was in a sparsely inhabited region known as the Afar triangle. It was uncomfortably close to Eritrea, where insurgents, in revolt against the Ethiopian government, might murder Johanson and his associates if they came across them.

Despite the discomforts and danger, Johanson had never felt better. His party was looking for fossils of hominids, early human ancestors and their relatives, and in the preceding weeks had found several. On this particular morning Johanson had already collected some superb antelope and baboon fossils and was suffused with a feeling that sometimes seizes field anthropologists —a feeling that this was going to be a lucky day.

Before returning to the camp for lunch, however, he strolled a few yards away over a small rise in the ground. This area had been scrutinized intensively on previous occasions by other members of his group. But on a hunch Johanson decided to have another look at it. The first thing he saw was a small arm bone lying on the ground.

"That's a hominid arm," he said.

"No it's not," said his companion. "It's too small. It's a monkey's arm."

Unconvinced, Johanson went over to pick it up. Lying next to it were some bits of skull. Intently, he began to examine the surrounding

Lucy's three-million-year-old skeleton consists of more than 60 separate pieces of bone. She is by far the most nearly complete pre-sapiens specimen ever found. Unfortunately, large parts of her cranium are missing.

ground and was able to spot other bits of bone: some vertebrae, limb-bone fragments, a piece of a lower jaw. Wildly excited now, he took his finds back to camp, returning the next day with a crew for a detailed sifting of the area.

After three weeks of work, Johanson had recovered about 40 per cent of a complete hominid skeleton. He was dumbfounded. He had something that paleoanthropologists the world over had been seeking for more than a century but never had found: one reasonably intact skeleton from a single individual, with enough parts preserved to show how everything fitted together, confirming for the first time without a shadow of a doubt the shape and size of a small, erect and exceedingly ancient hominid.

Small and ancient it was, almost beyond belief. It stood scarcely three and a half feet tall and appeared to be more than three million years old. The shape of its pelvis established that it was a female—not a little girl but a fully grown woman (if, indeed, the word "woman" could be applied to something so small and so remotely human). It was given a scientific specimen number: AL 288-1, but somewhere along the line it picked up the nickname of Lucy.

AL 288-1: A NEW HUMAN ANCESTOR?

Lucy was a peculiar little creature. She did not exactly resemble any of the other hominid fossils that have been found in Africa during 50 years of intensive search and that collectively bear the name of Australopithecines. She dated back further than nearly all of them, was notably smaller and had much smaller teeth. Still, she had much in common with the Australopithecines. That Lucy was a hominid—a creature related to men—and possibly a human ancestor was pretty certain. She was no ape. She was shaped very much like a very small human being, and she walked around on two legs.

The scientific furor over Lucy may seem surprising. During the past couple of decades, in which the rate of new hominid discoveries in Africa has been accelerating, there has been a steady stream of articles and books about them. The result has been a general impression that old hominid bones are lying all over Africa and

are as common there as junked cars are in the United States. Nothing could be more wrong.

It is true that good fossils of *Homo sapiens,* the species of human that exists today, are fairly common, some going back nearly 300,000 years, when *Homo sapiens* first appeared on the scene. But back of *sapiens* there has long been a severe dearth of fossils. Only during the last 75 years or so, as a result of careful search in Europe, Asia and Africa, have some bits and pieces of an older type gradually been found. These were at first variously called Java man, Peking man, and so on, each given its own Latin name. Recent studies have discarded those names. Experts now recognize that the names' owners all belong in a single species. Accordingly they have been given the label *Homo erectus,* to indicate that they were true men *(Homo),* erect-walking men *(erectus),* ancestral to modern humans but different enough to be put into a different species. *Homo erectus* first appeared more than a million years ago and began to disappear about 300,000 years ago as he was gradually replaced by *Homo sapiens.*

Going back even further in time, looking for ancestors of *Homo erectus,* the picture becomes even more cloudy. The first hint of something older came from South Africa in 1924 with the

Eight major hominid sites have been found on the shores of extinct lakes that were strung along the 1,500-mile stretch of the Great Rift Valley (shown in gray), from the Afar desert region of Ethiopia south beyond Nairobi in Kenya.

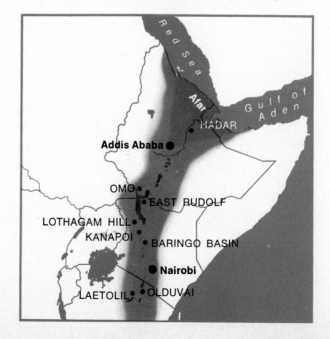

The flat Afar plain, part of which was once an immense lake bed, has eroded into gullied badlands, revealing ash layers from old volcanoes, and sediments that have washed down from the Ethiopian highlands. The lowest of the strata in these dusty valleys are more than three million years old.

Recent erosion reveals the fossil of a turtle preserved in its original shape in the lake sediment. Such sediments, gently deposited in still water, account for the unusually good condition of the fossils that abound at Hadar.

discovery of a strange little skull by the South African anatomist Raymond Dart. Dart's skull, while it had teeth that resembled the teeth of men, was otherwise so primitive and small-brained that many scientists tended to dismiss it as an odd ape or baboon of some sort. In the face of a good deal of skepticism, Dart insisted that it was not an ape but a hominid, that it walked erect and might even be a human ancestor. He conceded, however, that it was too primitive to qualify as human, a member of the genus *Homo.* He therefore assigned a new genus for it: *Australopithecus,* and gave it the species name *africanus.*

The identification of *Australopithecus africanus*—the southern ape from Africa—was a giant step in tracing hominid development, for Dart's claim was ultimately sustained when more Australopithecine fossils began to turn up in four other sites in South Africa. How old these were has never been exactly determined. They come from beds of limestone that are impossible to date by any of the measuring techniques paleoanthropologists rely on. But by studying the fossils of other animals found with them, scientists have been able to assign a rather uncertain age of two million years to some of them.

As the supply of South African Australopithecine fossils grew, it became increasingly clear that there were two kinds: a small slender "gracile" type that weighed about 80 pounds and stood not more than four and one half feet tall, and a larger "robust" type that weighed perhaps 100 to 150 pounds.

NEW FIND RESURRECTS OLD QUESTIONS

Good reconstruction of the two types has been extremely difficult, however, because most of the South African fossils were fragments, many of them badly worn, and because nearly all of them were teeth, with most of the rest of the skeleton entirely missing. This raises some tough questions about the relationship of the two:

Were they separate and distinct species existing at the same time?

Were they separate and distinct species existing at different times?

Were they males and females of a single species?

Arguments in support of each of these positions have been made. None is entirely satisfactory because of the poor quality and lack of completeness of the fossils and because of that balky problem of dating. If the ages of two closely allied extinct organisms are not known—and their ancestors or descendants are also not known—it is sometimes next to impossible to establish their relationship.

A breakthrough on dating came in 1959 when archeologist Mary Leakey found the skull of a robust Australopithecine in the Olduvai Gorge in Tanzania while working there with her late husband Louis Leakey. Thanks to the presence in the gorge of a layer of volcanic ash—which can be accurately dated—it was possible to establish the age of her find at about 1.7 million years. Since then important hominid finds have been made at Omo in southern Ethiopia and on the eastern shore of Lake Rudolf in northern Kenya. These are now being analyzed by paleoanthropologists. As in South Africa, there appear to have been both gracile and robust types. For many of them, reliable dates can be assigned, indicating without question that at least two types coexisted in the north for well over a million years prior to 1.5 million years ago.

Two types in the north and two in the south. How orderly.

Unfortunately not. On better acquaintance it became clear that the northern and southern types did not match each other all that well. The robust type in the north was super-robust, distinct from its cousin in the south. The gracile specimens in the north were even more perplexing. They did not even resemble one another. Some bore a close resemblance to their small South African counterparts. Others, though also small, were more manlike than any Australopithecine, with much larger brains. The suspicion kept growing that they might not have been Australopithecines at all but were dimly emerging *hominids*—creatures that stood on the misty edge between pre-men and men.

Louis Leakey thought so. He found the skull of one of those advanced gracile fossils in the Olduvai Gorge and promptly christened it *Homo habilis,* handy man, because of the great quantity of stone tools that had been found with it.

So—are there one, two, three or four kinds of Australopithecines in Africa?

Is one of them *Homo*?

For several years, the world of paleoanthropology has been struggling to answer those two questions, trying desperately to digest the new evidence that is pouring in as new finds are made. And at this point it becomes appropriate to ask why, if so much new fossil evidence *is* pouring in, the questions cannot be answered.

NOT MORE BUT BETTER

There are several reasons. One lies in the quality of the finds. Nine out of every 10 Australopithecine fossils is a tooth, and not always a very good tooth at that. Everything else exists in bits and pieces, some of them mere nubbins. Those bits and pieces are scattered over Africa and through more than a million years of time. They come from hundreds of different individuals: a tooth here, a bit of jaw there, a fragment of skull or pelvis from somewhere else. Nowhere is there anything resembling a complete Australopithecine skeleton. In fact, a great many parts of the Australopithecine bony structure have never been found at all. And in spite of the seeming plethora of finds, the pieces are actually still extremely rare. All of them—every last one—would fit in a single small closet. Reconstructing entire individuals—let alone several kinds of individuals—solely from the contents of that one closet is a task of stupefying difficulty.

What had to be found was not just *more* fossils but *better* fossils. With all that in mind, it is now possible to step back and be properly respectful when Don Johanson lays his fantastic find—Lucy—on the table. As a fossil among other fossils, Lucy is a glittering Kohinoor among diamond chips. Because her skeleton was nearly complete, answers to some critical questions about the true shapes and dimensions of early hominids, and ultimately their relationships to one another, are bound to be learned when plaster-cast copies of Lucy's bones are made and distributed among scientists for study. At the moment, just what Lucy is remains something of a puzzle. Those most interested in her can only

The first of three hominid jaws that he found during one 24-hour period is examined by Alemeyhew Asfaw, a gifted fossil hunter who was assigned to the Taieb-Johanson group as the official Ethiopian government representative.

wait to examine her, and congratulate Johanson on his luck in finding her.

Of course, there was more than mere luck involved. A whole chain of events had to be linked together to place Johanson in the Afar triangle—and in a particular spot in the triangle—on that memorable day.

The first link in the chain is a French geologist named Maurice Taieb, who was acquainted with the Afar through some geological studies he had been making there. Portions of the Afar are apparently the bed of a very large lake long since dried up. One section of it, along the Awash River at a place called Hadar, is cut by a large number of gullies, old stream beds that had sliced down through the layers of silt, volcanic ash and other material washed down from nearby mountains over a long period. Looking at

Lucy's bones get a preliminary sorting out by their finder, Don Johanson. Johanson, 32 years old, teaches anthropology at Case Western Reserve University in Cleveland, Ohio, and began hunting hominids only in 1970.

At the bottom of a Hadar gully, Ethiopian workmen sift material from a fossil-rich hillside through two table sieves. They do it painstakingly, a shovelful at a time, so that they will not lose even the smallest of fragments.

those layers, Taieb realized that they could probably be dated—and that this would facilitate the dating of any fossils found in them. The next thing that caught his eye was the great number of animal fossils at Hadar. They were all over the place, lying on the ground, working their way out of various strata.

The third thing that impressed him was their remarkable state of preservation. Most fossils are badly damaged by the time they are found —crushed, broken, rolled along in streams so that all of their delicate parts are gone and the rest blurred by ages of abrasion. Although Taieb was not a bone man, he could recognize that this was not the case here. Hadar had apparently been a lake shore, perhaps a wide marshy one where the rate of water flow was negligible. Anything that died fell into the mud on the spot and was gradually covered and protected by silt without being damaged at all. Taieb correctly reasoned that Hadar would be a superb place for a paleontologist to work. Much could be learned about the evolution of various kinds of animals there. If hominid fossils were found, that would be a bonus.

Taieb knew Johanson. He described the Afar to him, pointing out that if there were hominid fossils there, they would probably turn out to be exceptionally well preserved. Johanson was persuaded. The two raised some money, and in 1972, joined by the French paleoanthropologist Yves Coppens, went to the Afar for five weeks of what Johanson now calls blitz paleoanthropology. They drove rapidly about, locating sites and collecting a few outstanding fossils. They spent three days at Hadar, confirmed that it was probably the richest of the sites, and decided to go back with a larger group the following year.

What excited Johanson was not only the quality of the fossils he collected (they electrified scientists in 1973 when he showed slides of some of them at a conference in New York), but also Taieb's pronouncements about the age of the deposits at Hadar. Almost all past Australopithecine finds had been made in deposits from the Pleistocene Age, which goes back only two million years. Back of that, into the Pliocene, things were pretty much of a blank. It was the desire to reach into the Pliocene that had sparked a large international expedition, under the direction of F. Clark Howell, the American anthropologist, to the Omo River a few years before, and had sent Richard Leakey prospecting in East Rudolf. Both places turned out to be productive of late Pliocene fossil material that appeared to be at least three million years old. At Hadar, also, Taieb assured Johanson, there would be accessible layers that were at least three million years old, and perhaps considerably older.

FIRST STEP: GOOD DATES

In 1973 the two men enlarged the scope of their activities. They formed the International Afar Research Expedition, raised more money, and recruited other scientists and some graduate students. The 1973 expedition was devoted largely to making some valuable collections of mammal fossils, notably antelopes, elephants and pigs. The deposits proved to be between 300 and 400 feet deep. They were indeed Pliocene—three million years old, and older. Most important, several volcanic episodes had occurred during a relatively short period of time, each one depositing a layer of ash that, when tested in the laboratory, could provide a reliable date. Once good dates had been secured from those layers, the age of a fossil found between any two of them could be calculated with an error of 50 to 100,000 years. This translates into a possible time error of only two or three per cent, nearly unbelievable accuracy for events so remote in time. Since age is all-important in fossil studies, the extreme precision of this multilayered volcanic-ash yardstick was certain to be of incalculable value.

That year Johanson made the first of his hominid finds. They were encouraging because they confirmed that Hadar was the right place to concentrate on. The finds themselves were not spectacular: a piece of skull and some leg-bone fragments—although the latter were interesting in being very small; they came from a leg about half the size of that of a modern man. This raised the problem of whether they were hominid at all. Some members of the expedition thought that they could only be the leg bones of a monkey, but Johanson decided that their shape indicated

Four Hominid Types Compared

The differences between Lucy, two kinds of Australopithecines and modern man are shown in these reconstructions. The solid orange indicates bones that are known definitely from fossils; outlined in orange are bones that would not be visible in this view; the forms of remaining parts were deduced from studies of comparative anatomy. The Australopithecines are composites from scores of individuals; their overall shape and articulation are correspondingly less sure than are Lucy's, prepared from the surprisingly complete remains of a single individual. The Australopithecine specimens are superior to Lucy in one respect—the skulls are better preserved.

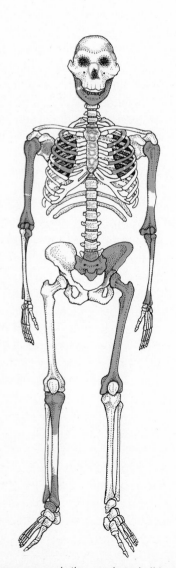

Lucy, fully grown, was only three and one half feet tall and probably weighed 45 to 50 pounds. Her discovery raises the possibility that a small creature like Lucy may have been ancestral both to the Australopithecines and to man.

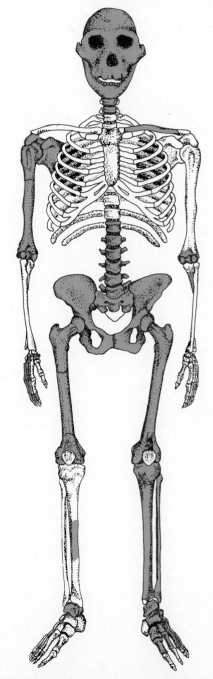

Australopithecus africanus, about four and one half feet tall, has been put together from bits and pieces found in East and South Africa. It has been considered by many anthropologists to be ancestral to Homo sapiens.

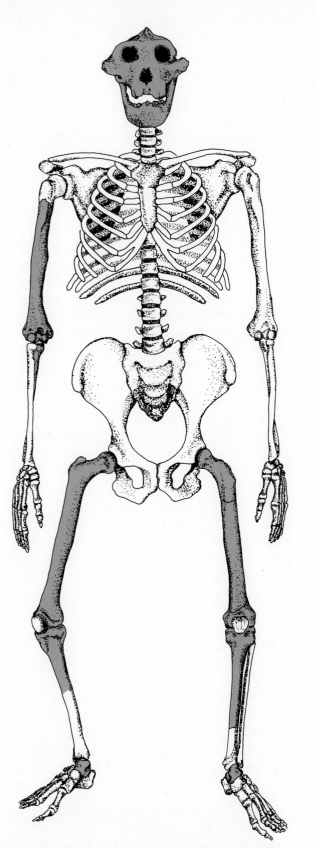

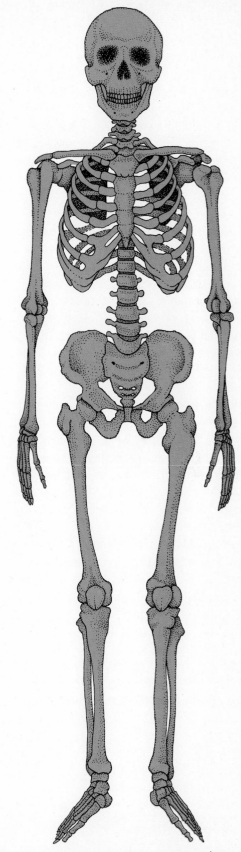

The super-robust Australopithecus boisei, discovered in East Africa, was five and one half feet tall, heavily built, with long arms and legs that bowed somewhat. It has never been considered to be a human ancestor.

Modern man betrays his resemblance to Australopithecus africanus in the shape of his pelvis and in the way the bones of his leg slant inward slightly. Like Homo sapiens, africanus probably walked erectly and with great ease.

that their owner had been a two-legged walker and could not have been a monkey. The expedition closed its books on 1973 with high hopes for the following year.

But by 1974 the Eritrean insurgent movement had grown. Bands of killers were operating on the edge of the Afar. Ethiopian politics were in a tumult. Johanson and Taieb considered giving up the expedition entirely, but the pull of Hadar was too great. They had the money, they had the experienced staff they needed, and they reasoned that the Afar people themselves would help protect them. The Afar are nomadic tribesmen. They move slowly about in their barren land, their lives bound to herds of camels, goats and sheep. The living is hard. The people are isolated and are extremely suspicious of strangers. They knew Taieb well and would not molest him, but they certainly would resent any Eritrean insurgents who penetrated their territory. Johanson and Taieb decided to go back. The Ethiopian government contributed a member, Alemeyhew Asfaw, whose ability to spot hominid fossils amounted to genius.

Within a week of their having settled in at Hadar, Alemeyhew Asfaw justified his reputation by coming up with part of a jaw containing two teeth. This find was reassuring because it helped confirm Johanson's assertion that last year's leg bones came from a hominid. The teeth in Asfaw's find were definitely hominid teeth.

A day later Asfaw ran into camp, shouting that he had found another fossil. The party rushed out to the little depression where it lay—since christened Hominid Valley. Sure enough, it was the entire half of an upper jaw containing a full complement of very small teeth, the smallest fossil hominid teeth that all those crowding around to look had ever seen.

Suddenly Asfaw shouted: "I've got another one." Not 30 feet from his second find, Asfaw's superb eye had spotted a third jaw, this one complete with all its 16 teeth. Within scarcely 24 hours, one man had made three brilliant discoveries, finding what others had sought for years, many unsuccessfully for a lifetime.

The three finds immediately raised some problems. There was no question that they were hominid, but what kind of hominid? They were not all alike. The first jaw seemed to bear resemblances to robust Australopithecine jaws. But the other two were smaller. Gracile Australopithecine jaws?

The longer Johanson looked at the new finds the more one problem gnawed at him. The size of the front teeth relative to the size of the back teeth seemed wrong. In all Australopithecines the front teeth are markedly smaller than the back teeth. However, as man begins to emerge, the front teeth that emerge with him are large in proportion to the size of his molars.

In those two smaller Hadar jaws the front teeth were relatively large.

The implications were staggering. Were the Hadar specimens *Homo*? Could *Homo*—something recognizable as a human being—conceivably have existed three and one half million years ago? It seemed beyond the bounds of credibility, but there lay the evidence on the table. Johanson thought long and deeply about it. Finally he decided that Mary and Richard Leakey should examine the fossils.

ADVICE FROM THE EXPERTS

The reputation of the Leakeys as Australopithecine experts is legendary. Mary Leakey had worked alongside her husband for nearly forty years in Olduvai, works there still, found the first hominid skull there, and has since become the world's leading authority on early hominid tools. Her son Richard, during only eight years' work at East Rudolf in Kenya, has, with his team, found more—and better—Australopithecine and early *Homo* fossils than any other man living or dead. Between them they were on intimate terms with all the East African fossils and had a nodding acquaintance with some of the South African ones.

Most important, some of Richard's most recent finds indicated that he, too, was the possessor of some Plio-Pleistocene fossils that he was willing to identify as *Homo*. He has made no attempt to give specific names to these, being by preference a simplifier rather than one who rushes to put different name tags on everything he discovers. His concern is in making sure that those very early borderland fossils contain enough *Homo* traits to allow them to fall legitimately into an overall basket labeled *Homo,* and not into some other basket labeled Australopithecine or pre-*Homo*—and now Don Johanson was faced with the same problem.

It is not an easy problem. In the first place, as Leakey points out, there is no official agreement on what *Homo* is. There has never been a congress of experts assembled to spell out that crucial point. As a result, an expert on the brain might (and probably would) decide that any two-legged creature with a brain capacity in excess of 650 cubic centimeters was a man. An expert on teeth might insist that brain capacity was secondary in importance and that the real clincher would be the relative size of front to back teeth. And so on. In short, agreement was needed on what measurements and characteristics made man-emerging a man. Pending settlement of that question, Johanson asked the Leakeys to Hadar. They came. He showed them his collection of jaws, now augmented by several more found by other members of the expedition in the days after Asfaw's sensational three-strike.

"They should be assigned to *Homo,*" said Richard after examining them.

Mary agreed.

A paleontologist who had come along with them confirmed Johanson's estimate of about three million years.

The Leakeys went back to Nairobi. The next morning Johanson went strolling in the hot sun and found Lucy.

What is Lucy? She is a hominid; her teeth indicate that. She is a female; her pelvis indicates that. She walked erect; her pelvis and legs indicate that. She was about 20 years old when she died; her recently emerged wisdom teeth and the stage of development of leg-bone growth indicates that. She lived in a marsh or on the edge of a lake; geology indicates that—and in a most interesting way. The material washed down in her direction from the Ethiopian highlands during the millennia has sorted itself out according to size. Large boulders and cobbles lie near the foot of the escarpment. Farther out on the plain, toward what was once the Afar lake, carried farther because they were smaller and hence more easily

transportable by water, are pebbles. Still farther, on what was once a lake shore, is fine sand and silt. Farthest of all, carried in suspension in minute particles by languidly moving water, is clay. The clay long ago settled in the center of the lake and contains no mammal fossils. The great abundance of them is in the sandier stuff at the lake's edge. And that is where Lucy was found.

A LUCKY BURIAL

So much for how Lucy lived; how did she die? Quietly—either from drowning or disease. There are no marks of a predator's teeth on her bones. She simply sank down and was covered up. Some three million years later, she began to emerge again. About half of her was lying on or just under the surface of the ground when Johanson found her. Unfortunately missing were large pieces of her skull, which makes accurate calculation of her brain capacity impossible. If Johanson had arrived five years earlier, he now remarks, he might have found the skull intact. But five years later he might not have found Lucy at all. Occasional flash floods could have scattered her irretrievably.

Is Lucy a member of the genus *Homo*? Johanson says no. She is too small, he thinks. Certainly she was not as advanced as *Homo* specimens that Richard Leakey has found at Lake Rudolf. They were at least a foot taller than she, weighed half again as much and had larger front teeth.

If not *Homo,* is Lucy an Australopithecine? Maybe not, says Johanson. Once again she is too small, far smaller than most of the gracile specimens so far found. That raises the possibility that she may be an example of an older, smaller line of beings from which both Australopithecines and men sprang. If that is so, then the recently popular idea that man is descended directly from Australopithecines may have to go out the window. The family tree would then have to be redrawn to show Lucy and her kind as representatives of a long-enduring line of very small, very old ancestral types—perhaps a kind of root stock from which several branches sprouted. There would be branches for the Australopithecines: one for the gracile type; another for the robust type (with possibly a twig for the super-robust); and there would be a branch for man.

In other words, something resembling Lucy may have begun to appear as early as five, 10 or even 15 million years ago. As the millennia rolled by, creatures that would lead to Australopithecines of whatever sort would have begun to differentiate themselves. So would men. In that scenario, Lucy would be a very late example of an ancestral type persisting on into a newer world dominated by those new-style Australopithecines and those new-style men. The important evolutionary splitting that had been accomplished by her ancestors would have taken place several million years earlier. Lucy herself would be an anachronism, a hanger-on. She would be at a dead end, ancestral to nobody. She would be about to become extinct.

LUCY: A FOREBEAR OR A DEAD END?

At this stage in the game it is straining things a bit to try to fit Lucy too exactly on the human family tree. Moreover, speculation about what she is clouds the greater value that she and the other Afar finds represent here and now.

Foremost is the extraordinary completeness of Lucy's skeleton. The significance of that fact alone cannot be overemphasized. No longer is it necessary to guess what the shape of an early hominid leg was by trying to assemble one from fragments of a dozen individuals. Such assembly always carries a large grain of uncertainty with it. Variability within a species, and the possibility of more than one species (the robust and super-robust Australopithecines, for example) can never leave the conscientious scientist wholly satisfied with his reconstruction. Only when all the leg bones are found in one place, lying next to a pelvis, ribs, vertebrae, arm bones, a jaw —with no parts of a second or third individual mixed in—can there be the kind of astonished "At last, here it all is, no more guessing needed" that Lucy evokes in the paleoanthropologist.

Second, now that Lucy's shape is certain, all sorts of valuable spinoffs in the realm of behavior should follow. To name just one: her clear contribution to the controversial matter of erect walking—just when and how did human ancestors get up on their hind legs and become true walkers? Lucy's pelvis and leg bones have not yet been studied by experts in locomotion, but when they are it should be possible to determine what some already suspect: that, while she did walk upright, she was not a wholly bipedal, completely terrestrial, tree-free creature. The bones aside, suspicion persists that any three-foot-tall, erect walker might have been too small to survive intact on the ground and might have had to resort to the trees regularly for safety. Nevertheless, the fact that she could walk reasonably well on two feet leads to a further inference about Lucy's behavior. She was probably a social animal; when on the ground she always moved in the company of a troop of others of her kind for mutual protection.

The third kind of help in unraveling the hominid triangle does not come from Lucy at all but from the other jaws found by the Afar group, from a fantastic haul of animal fossils, and from the layer cake of volcanic ash deposits at Hadar.

Seemingly unrelated pieces of data have a way of coming together like pieces in a jigsaw puzzle if other pieces can be found to link them together. Afar presents several such new linking pieces. There are whole sequences of elephant, antelope and pig fossils that show not only how evolution was proceeding in those animals, but also when it took place and how fast it was happening. Analysis of this material will someday throw light on the climatic variations over a considerable period of time in Ethiopia, and their possible effect on the evolution not only of other animals but also of hominids.

Equally important, linkups of the Afar finds with similar animal fossil sequences from other parts of Africa will begin to be possible—with Omo in southern Ethiopia, with East Rudolf in Kenya. Information gained at any of those places will benefit all of them. Eventually a sufficiently rich picture of what was going on among animals during the Plio-Pleistocene may make it possible to transport a large hunk of this jigsaw puzzle bodily to South Africa to look for fits among the fossil animals found there. If significant matchups appear, the riddle of dating the South African hominids may begin to unravel, and the question of just who *robustus* and *af-*

Protectors of the paleontologists, Afar tribesmen gather to swap camels, goats and news at a weekly highland market. The Afar, though well disposed toward Johanson and Taieb, were extremely suspicious of other strangers; as a result, scientists were guarded from potential enemies.

ricanus were may finally be answered. In fact, newly discovered hominid fossils from the north may already be on the way to providing an answer. Some of Richard Leakey's latest finds from East Rudolf appear to bear the label of *africanus,* as does a collection of separate teeth from Omo—all two to three million years old.

Johanson's other jaws, the ones that Leakey recognized as *Homo,* what do they say? Simply that man is old, very old, far older than anyone could have dreamed a couple of decades ago. Richard Leakey has excellent skull specimens of a comparable age that have been found at Lake Rudolf. They are as large-brained as any *Homo habilis.* If *habilis* qualifies as a man, so must they. That is fantastic. It means that men coexisted with Australopithecines in Africa for at least a couple of million years, perhaps for considerably longer. It means that a human being may well have looked Lucy in the eye—and not recognized her as his own evolutionary grandmother. His kind may even have exterminated her kind.

That ever-backward stretching of those beings that science is willing to call men cannot go on forever. Somewhere there must be a cutoff point, a point at which some combination of small size, small brain and inability to stride freely on two legs obscure the signs of emerging humanness. But how much obscuring does it take to hide which qualities of emergence?

That is what the conference that Leakey and Johanson have been talking about must decide. Only then can science agree on a formal definition of what makes man a man. Only then will it be possible to assign universally agreed-on names and time spans to the kinds of men who walked the earth a million or more years ago. A beginning and a cutoff date, for example, and general agreement on his physical dimensions are needed for *Homo habilis,* a fellow whose credentials are somewhat clouded at the moment. The same thing goes for those older hominids from Afar and East Rudolf. Are they really the same as *habilis,* or different? Is either of them a true man? If not, who is the ultimate ancestor? Only better knowledge—and agreed-on parameters—can answer those questions.

For Lucy, a name for her too. Until then we must settle for what Johanson has been calling her: a Plio-Pleistocene hominid, surely too fuzzy a title to be borne long by that unique—and important—little lady.

Harnessing the Wind

While a frantic search continues for fuels to supply the world's voracious appetite for energy, an ancient—and obvious—source of power is being rediscovered: wind. It is free and nonpolluting. These cheery qualities have inspired engineers, scientists and some inventive ecologists to build devices that turn generators with wind rather than fossil or nuclear fuel. The largest attempt to harness the wind is financed by the government, whose giant windmill *(page 39)* was to begin generating electricity in September, but even more grandiose efforts *(pages 40-41)* are planned by wind-power advocates.

Windmills are second only to water wheels as man's most ancient source of mechanical energy. By the 17th Century, Holland was dotted with nearly 8,000 windmills—much like the French example at right—that cut timber and milled grains. Windmills were a valued source of electricity in rural areas of the United States from the 1920s until the 1950s, when government-sponsored rural utility networks made them obsolete.

Building wind machines is one thing; making them economical is another. For while the wind is free, wind power is not. The force of wind is diffused over broad areas, so that a single windmill of old-fashioned size can intercept only enough to power one pump or millstone; to produce electricity on a utility plant scale would require 2,000 huge machines. And what do you do when the wind does not blow? Farm windmills have been connected to storage batteries. More complex solutions use windmills to produce chemical fuels that make electricity. But the prize for imagination goes to a group of Wisconsin inventors who connected a wind generator to an electric meter. When the wind blows, the scientists draw current from the windmill; any excess current feeds back to the utility, running the meter backward and reducing their bill.

An 18th Century windmill, as depicted in the famous Diderot scientific encyclopedia, published in Paris in 1762, has a rotating conical turret that turns its blades into the wind. Their effective area is controlled by canvas sails, which can be furled or extended, like a ship's, to suit the breeze.

Windmills for the Backyard

That windmills are relatively easy to make is attested to by the many machines being built by ecology-minded tinkerers and engineers (three of those shown here are from a small scientific institution, Wisconsin's Windworks). These windmills are used to draw water or produce small amounts of electricity, and range in sophistication from the device at top right, with its rough canvas-covered sails, to the aerodynamic contraption on the bottom left-hand side of the opposite page, which was designed by an associate of Buckminster Fuller.

One of the most unusual is the one at right below, which is made of oil-drum halves. Unlike most, this windmill rotates on a vertical axis. Because the openings face away from each other, they can be spun by wind from any direction; conventional windmills must face into the wind.

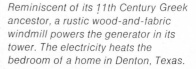

Reminiscent of its 11th Century Greek ancestor, a rustic wood-and-fabric windmill powers the generator in its tower. The electricity heats the bedroom of a home in Denton, Texas.

Vertically mounted windmills like this one in Wisconsin, made of old oil drums, are easy and cheap to make and for this reason are popular in underdeveloped countries, where they are used to pump water. The heavy drums spin too slowly, however, to make power generation practical.

*This experimental windmill, built by a ►
Wisconsin company called Windworks, is a fiberglass venturi tube, which is pinched in the middle to cause moving air to flow faster at that point. The venturi channels wind to a propeller mounted at the narrowest part.*

A scientist at Massachusetts' New Alchemy Institute carries the fabric-covered blades of a homemade windmill built for an exhibit. A larger version of this windmill pumps water for the Institute's fish farm.

In rural Wisconsin, a pickup truck tests a windmill that can be built from mail-order plans in around 150 hours. Tubular cowling houses a generator to convert wind energy into electricity, which is then stored in batteries.

Imaginative Designs from the Pros

A good deal more complex than the contraptions of backyard inventors are the professionally engineered windmills. Although bizarre-looking, these machines are so lightweight and sleekly shaped that they turn much faster and thus are able to produce more power than conventional designs. The 25-foot Sailwing (below, right) spins like an airplane propeller to produce enough electricity for a single house, while the counter-rotating propellers on the 36-foot-high windmill below at left yield enough power for five homes.

The most unusual of the new wind machines is the rig opposite, which consists of two integrated windmills—one with rotors shaped like the oil-drums on page 34, which start it spinning, the other with thin, light rotors, shaped like an egg beater, which spin fast enough to generate electricity sufficient to light a one-family home.

Designed by Princeton University aeronautical research engineer Thomas Sweeney, the Sailwing has hollow Dacron blades whose airplane-wing shape provides maximum spin with minimum weight. Larger-area Sailwings could eventually produce power for a number of families.

An international team of engineers built this unusual wind machine on the German island of Sylt in the North Sea. Its dual blades will produce more power than a single set, and by turning in opposite directions, they counteract the twisting torque that is generated by one-way rotation.

An engineer at Sandia Laboratories in Albuquerque, New ▶ Mexico checks egg-beater blades that spin on a vertical axis connected directly to a generator. This eliminates the complex gearing used by most horizontal-axis windmills to transmit wind-produced motion from blades to generator.

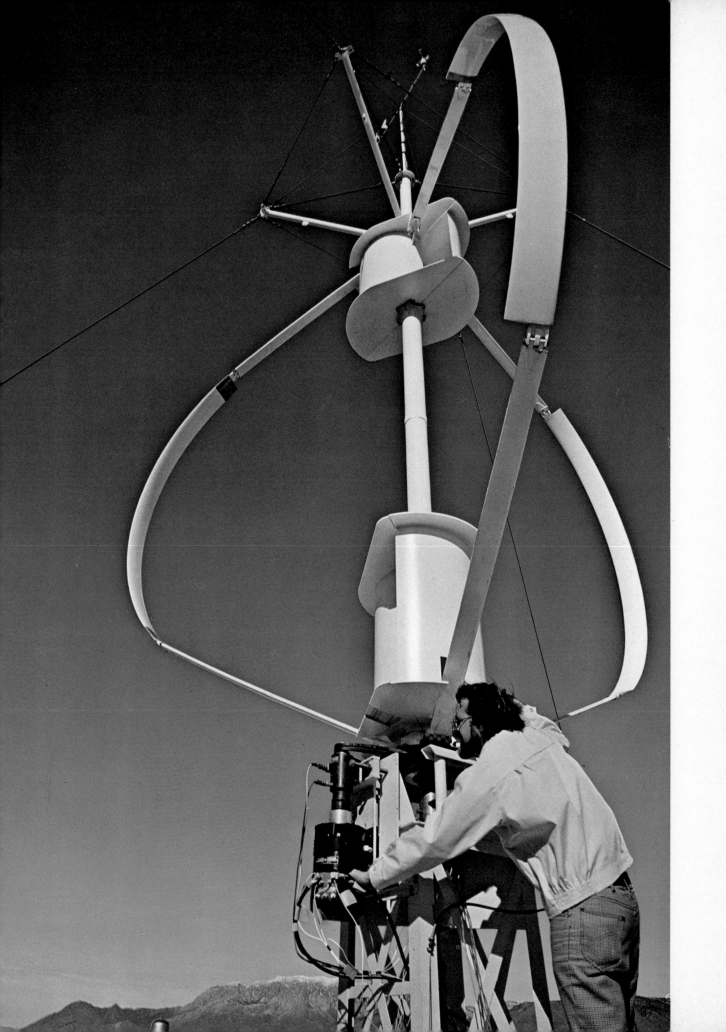

Massive Machines for Megawatt Power

If wind machines are ever to achieve their potential as a means of providing clean, inexpensive power to large communities, they will have to produce not just the kilowatts one house needs, but megawatts. A few devices that could be increased in size to produce megawatt-range power have already been built privately (above). But the major effort is supported by the government's Energy Research and Development Administration and is implemented by NASA, which called on the Lockheed-California Corporation to design and construct the blades of the large wind machine shown at right.

With wind turning its two 62.5-foot propellers, the machine has already produced enough electricity to light 30 homes. Scientists estimate that clustering 500 of these windmills could provide power for a town with a population of 50,000.

An aircraft mechanic turned inventor, Thomas Chalk of St. Cloud, Florida, works beneath his wind machine, whose 48 whirling blades are mounted like the spokes in a giant bicycle. Because of its many lightweight airfoil-shaped blades, Chalk's is one of the most efficient types of windmill. It extracts power at its rim, which spins faster than the central shaft, allowing the windmill to produce more electricity than a conventional machine of equal size.

Seated before a computer screen, a design engineer at Lockheed presses buttons on a small console to call up windmill-blade shapes that are stored in the computer's memory bank. Then he uses an electronic probe, called a light pen, to alter the shape of the blade—in effect he designs the blade on-screen. Once the engineer feels that he has the best possible design, he stores it in the computer. The computer then controls the machines that automatically cut templates used to fabricate the actual blade. Below, a workman begins riveting an aluminum skin around the tubular core of one blade, using as his guide the egg-shaped templates on which the core rests.

Grandiose Planning for the Future

Set up 69,000 windmills from cables suspended between 600-foot towers straddling the highways every three quarters of a mile over huge areas of the Midwest and keep the lights burning in Michigan and most of the Chicago area as well. Float 40,000 windmills off the Massachusetts coast and serve the power needs of New England. Erect 600,000 windmills on 300,000 square miles of the Great Plains and produce more than half of the power used in the United States.

These are not science-fiction schemes. Along with similar projects, they have been proposed in the last few years by serious scientists who think of the wind as an untapped energy source that should be harnessed on a grand scale.

The New England Offshore Wind Power Project *(right)*, the Great Plains and the Midwest concepts are the brainchildren of William E. Heronemus, Professor of Civil Engineering at the University of Massachusetts and an enthusiastic leader in the large-scale wind-power field. He has an exotic plan for storing up wind energy against times of calm. Wind-generated electricity would decompose seawater into its constituent atoms of hydrogen and oxygen. The hydrogen would be piped ashore and fed into fuel cells, which would convert the hydrogen into the electricity that consumers use.

Heronemus has estimated that if all the wind power available to the United States could be harvested, at least two trillion kilowatt-hours of electricity could be produced in a year—a figure equal to the total annual consumption of electricity in the United States in the early 1970s.

One of the possible windmill arrays considered by Professor Heronemus for his New England project calls for groups of 164 wind stations, each powered by three mills. The stations are floated on buoyancy spheres and generate electricity, which is channeled by interconnecting cables to a central station (at center, in this artist's concept). The central station contains electrolysis devices that use the electricity to extract hydrogen from seawater and it also provides living quarters for a resident crew. Most of the hydrogen is piped ashore as needed, with the excess stored in tanks on the sea bed. Professor Heronemus envisages 83 such multiple arrays strung along the New England shore.

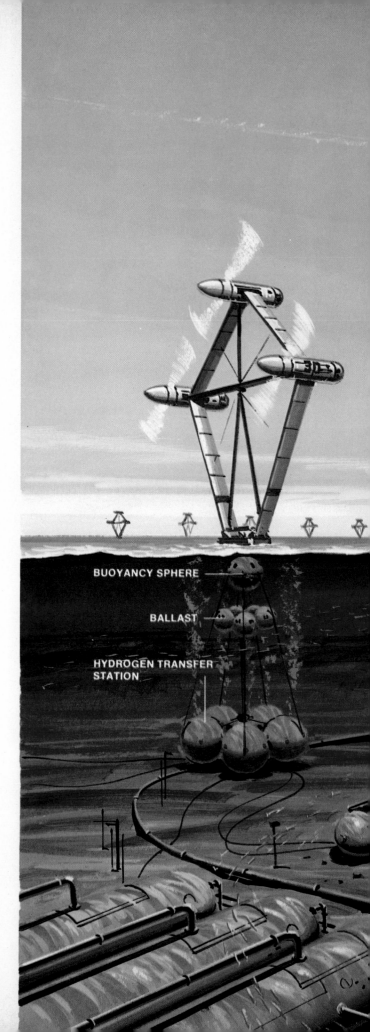

BUOYANCY SPHERE

BALLAST

HYDROGEN TRANSFER STATION

GENERATOR

LADDER INSIDE
ACCESS LEGS

MINISUB FERRY

ELECTROLYSIS STATION
AND LIVING QUARTERS

YDROGEN
STORAGE
TANKS

HYDROGEN PIPELINES

VALIGURSKY

41

A Miracle of Crossbreeding

MATING "INCOMPATIBLE" CELLS PROMISES WONDER CROPS

by Jonathan Norton Leonard

Man's invention of agriculture around 7000 B.C. showed him how to control the earth, and ever since then his numbers have been increasing, his control improving. Many people foresee an ultimate end to this process, and during the past few years pessimistic views of man's future food supply seem to have been the more numerous (it is hard to keep count of such things). But in 1975 some good news was coming out of laboratories around the world. It suggests that a second agricultural revolution, rivaling in significance the original one of 7000 B.C., may make it possible to mold new food plants to order, engineering them to have almost any desired qualities. Thus crop plants, the chief sources of human food, may be made to produce a great deal more of it than they do now.

The work that offers such high hopes concerns hybrids—the genetically mixed offspring of parents different from each other. But these hybrids are a very special sort. Over the last 16 years, scientists have learned to bypass traditional breeding methods by working directly with individual plant cells, and they believe they are now about to create hybrids that will be crosses not just of two close relatives but of two distinct species, like rice and soybean or wheat and clover. The new interspecies hybrids would combine the characteristics of both parents; because the parents were so different, the offspring might possess remarkable combinations of properties: They might need no fertilizer, or resist frost better, or produce more protein.

Until now, crosses between species seemed

This emerald glob, beginning to grow stems and leaves from an amorphous mass of cells, is an embryonic tobacco plant of a totally novel kind, heralding a new era in plant breeding. It was grown from the laboratory fusion of two cells, each taken from different tobacco species that do not cross in nature and it holds out the hope that cells of any plants can be crossed to build new hybrids.

almost impossible. Today, scientists in the United States, Canada and England are growing them in their test tubes. A good place to take a first look at this hopeful, new-style work with crop plants is the microbiological laboratory of K. N. Kao at Saskatoon, Saskatchewan. To a casual visitor's eye it is not a remarkable place. It occupies several smallish rooms in the Canadian government's Prairie Regional Laboratory and has the usual equipment of its field: a centrifuge, vibrating tables, a shiny metal sterilizer, many microscopes. Nothing exceptional appears even when Kao, a remarkably youthful 41-year-old biologist originally from China, shows little groups of plant cells, as many as 100 clustered together Most of these cells appear spherical and motionless when viewed through a microscope. A few seem to be dividing, building new walls across their middles.

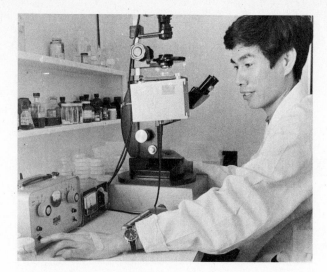

Operating a microscope-camera combination, controlled by the device at left, Kuo Nan Kao, a leader in cellular hybridization, prepares to record the results of his work.

A SOYBEAN-BARLEY PLANT

However, the clusters of cells are unusual, Kao explains. He touches a covered plastic dish in which some of them are growing. "These," he says, "are descended from fused cells of soybean and barley." There is no hint in his soft voice—and indeed little enough in the austere scientific papers that record his progress—of the cells' significance. Yet the cells are those of a new grain crop that—if Kao ever gets it to mature—would combine the characteristics of a legume and a cereal. These two families of plants differ radically in many ways. The most important difference is the way they use nitrogen.

Nitrogen makes up some 78 per cent of the atmosphere and is vital for the growth of all plants, which must either take it in from the soil or from the air. Legumes—like clover, soybeans, beans and peas—take it from the atmosphere; they encourage nitrogen-fixing bacteria to form nodules on their roots, and these bacteria extract all the nitrogen the plant needs from the air that permeates the soil. Legumes need no special nitrogen fertilizer. They thrive year after year without it, while grain crops such as wheat and barley quickly exhaust most of the soil's nitrogen and thenceforth give low yields.

A cross between a legume and wheat or bar-

ley like Kao's soybean-barley—"soyley" it might one day be called—ought never need any nitrogen fertilizer. By getting all it needs from the bacteria on its roots, as a legume does, it would keep producing, indefinitely, very large yields of a grain containing a lot of desirable protein. A dream crop like this might relieve the protein hunger that now afflicts most of the world's poor.

According to traditional genetic theory, this was an impossible dream—not because it called for a hybrid but because the parents were so dissimilar. Ordinary hybrids are fairly common. The very first domesticated plants, in fact, were probably the result of naturally occurring crosses that produced new plants different from their wildgrass parents. The hardy wheat that has been cultivated for making bread flour in the Middle East since about 6000 B.C. is now known to be a hybrid of a wild wheatlike grass called emmer and some other wild grass possessing cold-resistant qualities.

The earliest farmers learned to create deliberate hybrids, and with the development of genetics in the 20th Century, this ancient practical art became a scientifically based business. Today much of the world's food comes from relatively recent breeds of hybrid plants. But these hybrids are almost all crosses between

Cells of such unrelated plants as barley (left) and soybean (right) have been crossed, but were not able to grow to maturity.

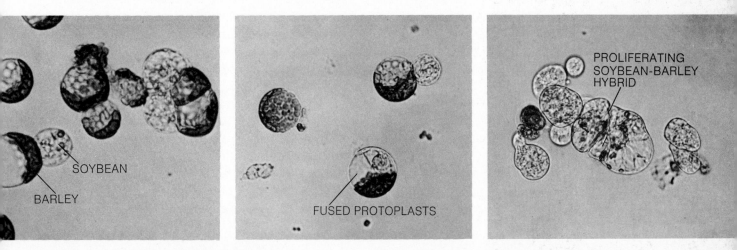

SOYBEAN

BARLEY

FUSED PROTOPLASTS

PROLIFERATING
SOYBEAN-BARLEY
HYBRID

Photomicrographs record the fusion of barley and soybean protoplasts—cells stripped of their protective walls. At left, the dark-rimmed barley protoplasts touch the lighter ones of soybean. Two of them fuse (center), though each retains its own nucleus. At right, the fusion is complete and the new hybrid cell has already proliferated. If cell proliferation could be continued to produce a complete plant, the result might be an invaluable new crop.

varieties of the same species; only rarely do different species interbreed. One recent—and valuable—example of crossed species is triticale, the new wheat-rye hybrid *(box, page 51).* The reason is simply the differences between species that emerge as their paths separate in the course of their evolution. Varieties become more and more distantly related as geography and climate encourage new adaptations—different flowering times, different methods of pollination, and incompatible pollen and eggs—that eventually lead to the formation of new species. Natural sexual interbreeding becomes forever impossible —even artificially.

The longer ago the evolution into distinct species, the more remote they are. And the more distant the relationship, the more formidable the barriers against sexual crossbreeding. The barriers between species of the same genus, let alone between such larger groups as families or orders, were considered all but inviolable—until the recent spate of research into cell hybridization revealed a means of crossbreeding, not plants themselves, but the genetic material inside their cells.

The new methods came about partly because the old, well-tried methods of breeding were so laborious and expensive. They took many seasons, demanded acres of land, good weather, irrigation and protection against disease. When breeders tried to create better strains of crops, they kept watching for natural variations, most of them involving a slight change in the genetic character of a single cell. If this cell developed into a plant or living twig, it might look different enough to attract attention. It would then be propagated to see whether it turned out to be a valuable new variety.

Even systematized and aided by modern techniques, this system required years of skillful effort—and considerable luck—to develop a useful new plant. An exception was the famous IR-8 strain of rice that increased the Philippines' production by 28 per cent in the early 1970s, the result of only two years' research. Was it possible, scientists asked themselves, to cut a few corners by working directly with plant cells?

Plant cells, like animal cells, contain all the ge-netic information needed to form an adult. Inside each cell are DNA molecules that serve as blueprints to guide the formation of all the parts making up the complete plant. Every cell of wheat, whether from root, stem or seed, has in it blueprints for every part; thus a single plant cell can grow into a complete plant.

Animal cells cannot ordinarily achieve such total regeneration *(How to Grow a New Leg, pages 94-103).* If cells are taken from under the skin of a man's hand, they can be kept alive, but they cannot be persuaded to grow into another man, and neither can living cells taken from other higher animals regenerate their kind. Plant cells can, however. A twig cut from a willow tree holds eagerly to life. If its base is poked into moist soil and left alone, it quickly turns itself into a small willow tree, with roots, trunk, leaves and everything else a young willow needs. A single cell from a willow can do the same thing if it is treated properly.

CARROTS MADE IMMORTAL

For a long time the proper treatment for single cells remained elusive. But in the 1930s two scientists in France found that small bits of carrot root put in a proper nutrient solution would grow indefinitely, though the natural life of a carrot plant is only two years. Descendants of those original carrot bits are still alive, and it is easy to make parts of them develop into whole carrots.

A good many plant cells have been made immortal in similar fashion, and it is generally assumed that all plant cells could be made to live forever if tended with sufficient skill and care. The starting point is to separate a very small piece of the plant and permit it to grow for a while in a nutrient solution. It will produce lumps or tufts of cells, called calluses, that are not organized into any specific part of a plant.

The cells multiply, and small bits of unusually desirable callus mass can be separated and treated with plant hormones and other chemicals that make them turn into plants with roots, stems and leaves. Such breeding is fast and easy. It is already used commercially to reproduce rapidly and surely such highly valued and difficult-to-raise plants as orchids.

A Brookhaven National Laboratory researcher inspects the fused cells of two tobacco species to see if stems and roots have appeared. The blurred flasks (foreground) are shaken to keep cells separate for experimental use.

Given the generative talents of any one cell, scientists guessed that if they could work with individual cells, they might be able to overcome the natural resistance of one species to another; they might be able to make the two link together in such a way that their internal genetic blueprints would mix to form the cell of a totally new hybrid that is impossible in nature.

This was all very well in theory, but the technical problems were formidable. Plant cells have hard outer coatings of cellulose, the tough material of wood, and are firmly welded together in a lattice-like arrangement, sometimes of amazing strength. Before individual cells can be used for experiments they must be separated from their fellows and stripped of their cellulose walls to form naked protoplasts. (Protoplasts retain all the abilities of the complete cell; they can regenerate their walls, divide and mature.) Then protoplasts of the two species must be pushed together so that they have a chance of uniting.

Cell-wall removal had been done mechanically around the turn of the century, but it was intricate and time consuming.

The present method of cell-wall removal was achieved for the first time in 1960 by Edward Cocking, now Professor of Botany at Nottingham University, England, but then a 28-year-old lecturer there. He had been struck by the fact that many fungi living on plants can break down their hosts into protoplasts by releasing two enzymes. One of these enzymes, pectinase, attacks the plant tissue by dissolving pectin, the substance that makes the tissue's cells hold to one another. The cells then move apart slightly, permitting a second enzyme, cellulase, to dissolve the cellulose in the cells' outer walls. When the cellulose is gone, the cells lose the angular shape that made them fit so neatly into their native tissues. Each turns roughly spherical and moves farther away from its neighbors. It is now a protoplast, a naked, vulnerable plant cell with nothing but a thin membrane around it.

By adapting nature's technique to the laboratory, Cocking and his associates devised a simple method of preparing protoplasts, a method since taken up by scientists in many countries to produce protoplasts from any species in which they were interested. The protoplasts can be preserved indefinitely in dishes of nutrient—coconut milk proved particularly effective—until they are stimulated by a hormone concentration that will allow them to mature into complete plants.

The next task was to get two protoplasts to fuse. For this to happen, the protoplasts, which are roughly spherical and would normally touch in just one place, had to be pressed together so that their external membranes would dissolve and their insides, including the DNA of the plants' genetic codes, would mix.

Once again, it was Cocking who led the way. By 1970, he had not only fused protoplasts taken from plants of the same species (onions in one set of experiments, oats in a second, tobacco in a third), he had also, briefly, fused the protoplasts of two different species, wheat and maize. His method involved immersing the protoplasts in a solution—he tried a number of different ones, of which sodium nitrate proved to be the

Tiny bits of carrot are punched out of carrot slices in an early experiment at Cornell University on growing whole plants from single cells. Such research, done in many different laboratories, developed techniques that led to methods for creating hybrids by crossing individual cells.

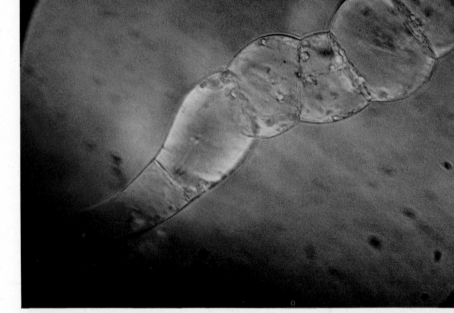

Having been shaken apart from its fellows in an udder-shaped flask like that shown opposite, a carrot cell multiplies in a special nutrient solution.

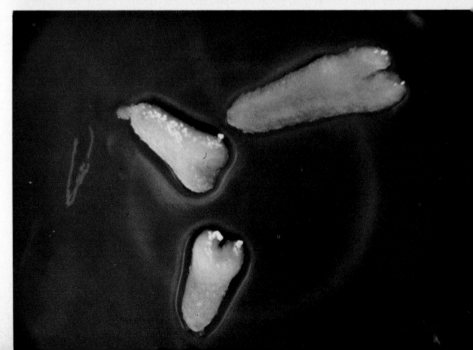

Three microscopic masses of tissue, each grown from one cell, begin to adopt the shape of carrot embryos.

A test-tube carrot plant, complete with stems, leaves and the beginnings of its edible root, grows alongside the flask containing the yellow masses of carrot pieces that form the starting point of this pioneering experiment.

49

best—that affected the electrical properties of their membranes, so that they attracted each other, touched, squeezed together and finally fused. Although only a small percentage of his protoplasts actually united, and even fewer divided, it was a genuine breakthrough. The avenue was now open, Cocking announced in a 1970 paper, for the production of "otherwise unobtainable hybrids which might be of great interest." Great interest, indeed.

The prospect was a dazzling one. Researchers seemed to be on the edge of creating hybrids from plants of any species, however distantly related they seemed. But there was a catch: None of the fused protoplasts would divide. They simply died long before they began to mature.

The problem was—and still is—that the protoplasts from every species require a slightly different nutrient solution, and hybrid protoplasts require different nutrients again. But of course no one knows in advance what combination of chemicals and hormones would be suitable. To get any protoplast to grow, therefore, demands a mass of trial-and-error experiments with different nutrients.

MAKING PROTOPLASTS MATURE

In the early 1970s, however, there were several species whose nutrient requirements were pretty well known. One was tobacco, which already had been grown from a single protoplast. It would not, perhaps, be too hard to persuade the protoplasts of two species of tobacco to fuse and mature, and in 1972, scientists at Brookhaven National Laboratory on Long Island began an experiment to achieve just that. The group, led by Peter Carlson and Harold Smith, was on fairly firm ground: The species used, *Nicotiana glauca* and *N. langsdorffi,* are among the few plants of different species that can be crossed sexually and thus can be assumed compatible.

Carlson and his group made protoplasts from leaves of both species, using the best methods available at the time, and then put samples of both into nutrient solutions. Many protoplasts joined to form single larger cells, some of which started to multiply by division. At least one was a true hybrid, made up of two protoplasts, one from each species (page 42). It was vigorous, multiplying quite rapidly and producing masses of calluses. When these were divided and given growth-promoting nutrients, some of them were able to grow small green shoots and, eventually, roots. They finally yielded full-sized plants like the one on page 53 that look to the layman something like commercial tobacco.

They are not really admirable plants. Growing in a Brookhaven greenhouse they look vigorous only to eyes that have never seen a thriving tobacco plant. They have an unpleasant ailment: callus-like tissue or tufts of small green shoots that keep appearing on the stems. They are not at all likely to be welcome in farmers' fields, but —as the first full-grown products of a two-species fusion—they have earned a hallowed place in tomorrow's textbooks.

Though of unlikely practical value, the Brookhaven hybrid roused great excitement in other laboratories where similar work was going on. At Saskatoon, Kao and his associates launched another attack on the two-species problem, using ideas of their own. They made protoplasts of many crop plants, including legumes and grasses other than barley and soybean.

Their procedure was about as follows. Small bits were taken from greenhouse-grown leaves, sterilized by brief treatment with alcohol, and the undertissue carefully peeled away. The separation of the leaf cells from one another was accomplished with pectinase while cellulase was used to dissolve the cellulose walls, stripping the cells to naked protoplasts in five to 24 hours. The protoplasts were separated from larger debris by a fine-mesh filter.

Then came a special trick developed at Saskatoon: the use of a chemical called polyethylene glycol, or PEG, to make the protoplasts stick to each other. (PEG alters the electrical charges that exist on the surfaces of all living cells and make some repel others. It is a common ingredient in cosmetics and hand creams, where it makes oil and water mix.) After the PEG helps two cells approach each other, it is cautiously removed by washing. The surfaces of the protoplasts then come even closer together, and when nearly all of the PEG is gone, they touch and

A Super Crossbreed Born by Accident

Triticale—a cross between wheat and rye—is the first successful man-made cereal, the only crop plant created by interbreeding two plants so different that each parent belongs to a separate genus. The success of the new supergrain, which combines wheat's high energy content with the ruggedness of rye, is astonishing; in 1974 a million acres were harvested in 52 countries. Oddly, this success owes nothing to the new-style genetic tinkering. It results from old-fashioned breeding: decades of work, thousands of experiments and much luck.

Triticale has been around since 1875, when a Scotsman, Stephen Wilson, fertilized wheat stigma with rye pollen and produced the stringy offspring that got its name from *Triticum* and *Secale,* the generic names of wheat and rye. Triticale proved an unprepossessing creation —weak-stemmed, late in maturing and low in yield. Worst of all, it suffered the fatal defect of most interspecies crosses: It could not reproduce itself. Each cell contained separate sets of genes, one from each parent, and these distinct chromosomes refused to combine.

In 1937 a major advance turned triticale from a scientific curiosity into a possible food source. In that year Pierre Givaudon, a French biochemist, found that a chemical called colchicine, derived from the autumn crocus, could make chromosomes double, giving a hybrid like triticale enough genetic material to stand a chance of reproducing itself. In the 1950s this discovery encouraged breeding experiments on triticale at the University of Manitoba and later at Mexico's International Maize and Wheat Improvement Center, where the pioneer of the "Green Revolution" in new crops, Norman Borlaug, runs the International Wheat Program.

The breakthrough came in 1967—by pure chance. In Borlaug's words: "One promiscuous, venturesome stray wheat pollen grain floated across the road and fertilized a sad but permissive, tall, degenerate triticale plant." A year later, the amazed scientists came across the second generation offspring: a strong-stemmed dwarf plant, reliable in its maturing time, almost completely fertile, yielding 50 to 60 per cent more than previous strains.

With this new variety, workers in Mexico and Manitoba further revamped triticale's genetics by crossbreeding. In 1974, advanced strains of triticale topped the highest recorded wheat yield by 15 per cent; it makes good pasta, pancakes, breakfast food and passable bread; it is fertile, matures early, resists disease well, grows in rough ground and has a strong stem. Though a product of traditional methods, triticale proves that species can cross, and it reinforces hopes that new lab techniques will create even more effective hybrids.

then fuse, forming a single spherical body as two falling drops of water do.

This operation Kao has now performed many times to form many different hybrids. Besides creating soyley, he has fused soybeans with corn and pea, pea with vicia (an herb), and clover with rape (an herb). Of his successful fusions, some have divided into as many as 100 cells, and the major problem now is one of finding the proper nutrients with which to stimulate healthy growth.

Though the practical applications of Kao's work lie some time in the future, one thing has become clear: The almost insurmountable barriers against crossing species are disappearing. It seems to make no difference how distantly related species are; as long as healthy protoplasts can be produced from them, crosses will be attempted. From now on, much research will go toward the selection of hybrids that would prove the most productive.

One of the most intriguing ideas now being pursued is a crop that boosts its own yields by retaining energy ordinarily lost in the process of growth. To live and grow, plants breathe in two quite different ways. During the day they take in carbon dioxide and release oxygen as they make sugars from the carbon dioxide and water. This is photosynthesis. But at the same time they take in oxygen to keep their normal life processes going, releasing carbon dioxide as waste. This respiration, as it is called, is essentially the reverse of photosynthesis but on a lesser scale, so that the difference between the carbon dioxide absorbed in photosynthesis and the smaller amount lost in respiration should, it seems, be available to fuel the plant's growth.

A STRANGE AND WASTEFUL CHARACTERISTIC

But it is not. There is a third system, one that seemed utterly baffling when it was first noticed in the late '50s. By this process, termed photorespiration, plants release large quantities of carbon dioxide under the influence of light, a reaction totally unconnected with the parallel release of carbon dioxide during respiration. This tremendous loss of an essential raw material involves a corresponding loss of potential productivity—that much less foodstuff per acre.

Could the lost carbon dioxide be saved somehow and used to increase the crop's yield? It could indeed, at least in theory. For plants do not photorespire with equal strength. Scientists divide them into two groups, and an understanding of the difference involves a tentative suggestion as to why such a strange and apparently wasteful device evolved. The less efficient plants —those that lose the most carbon dioxide in photorespiration—use a particular series of chemical reactions in photosynthesis. These reactions begin with the formation of acids having three carbon atoms; plants using them are known as C-3's, a group that includes most crop plants —tobacco, grains, soybeans and peanuts.

This type of plant, it is thought, evolved early in the earth's history, when the atmosphere contained less oxygen—and thus a greater proportion of carbon dioxide—than it does now. As these plants photosynthesized, they released oxygen and began to create today's atmosphere. But there was a catch: The oxygen, for reasons not fully understood, causes the plant to transform some carbon dioxide into the chemical glycolic acid, which later breaks down to release carbon dioxide in photorespiration and thus to lose material otherwise used in photosynthesis.

Later plants evolved more complex—and two or three times more efficient—means of coping with the increased oxygen supply. They evolved in their photosynthesizing machinery a way of concentrating carbon dioxide so that less of it was available for conversion into glycolic acid, and thus less would be lost in photorespiration. These plants—the C-4's, so called because the first compounds they form in photosynthesis have four carbon atoms—include a few crop plants, notably sugar cane and corn. If C-3 plants had the efficiency of C-4 crops, their yield could leap by anything up to 50 per cent.

New C-4 plants are only one among the many possibilities that excite scientists. Resistance to drought, disease, insects and cold, the ability to mature rapidly for multiple crops—even better flavor—all are qualities that could aid the world's overtaxed food supplies. Such dreams cannot be indulged too long, however. Perhaps man's newfound opportunity to use protoplasts as one attempt to slip around the barriers set up by nature is an unnatural thing that cannot be made to work. Perhaps it will work too well, creating useless plants so overwhelmingly vigorous that they do great damage as weeds.

But most biologists are optimistic. The obstacles they see ahead of them do not seem insurmountable, and the chances for both expected and unexpected triumphs are considered good. Almost every crop has something about it that cries for improvement. Corn is a fabulous producer, but it has little protein in its kernel, and what is there is not ideal for the human diet. It could be a better crop plant if it accepted nitrogen-gathering microbes on its roots. If a new corn variety produces more than 100 bushels of flavorful grain on each acre of ordinary land and does not call for any nitrogen fertilizer, it will be meeting the lower expectations of many practical biologists. They are hopeful men.

One of Brookhaven's hybrid tobacco plants looms up from a mass of other adult hybrids, tended here by biologist Nicholas Combatti. The hybrid, though apparently strong, is not really healthy: many of the stems produce tumors.

Sea Otters Vs. Man

ONCE RARE, THEY STEAL FISH

by Robert Wallace

On the coast of California the sea otter *(Enhydra lutris),* which had once been thought to be extinct there, was making a vigorous comeback. In mid-1975 some 1,700 of the animals could be seen frolicking offshore between Monterey Bay and Morro Bay. And since the sea otter is among the most interesting and appealing creatures in the world, it might be assumed that its comeback was being greeted with cries of delight. Actually it was being greeted, in certain influential quarters, with oaths and threats to kill the blighter.

The problem is that the sea otter is extremely fond of just the sort of expensive seafood—abalones, clams, crabs and lobsters—that human beings enjoy, and the otter is a far more efficient diver and forager than any commercial or sport fisherman. In areas where the otter has become reestablished abalones and clams have been virtually wiped out.

Today the otter, which has no natural enemies in the region, is doubling in population every 14 years and extending its range north toward San Francisco Bay at the rate of about a mile a month. If nothing is done to stop its relentless advance, the otter may ultimately wipe out the Dungeness crab as well—and the thought of San Francisco without cracked crab on its menu is as depressing as the notion of the city without its cable cars.

This is the second time in its nearly 230-year

About to munch on the clamlike innards of a sea urchin, a sea otter clamps the spiny echinoderm in its paws. The sea otter's fancy for seafood—including the same abalone, crab and clams prized by human beings—has made the once-scarce (and beloved) animal something of a pest.

acquaintanceship with white men that the innocent sea otter has been in trouble. Early in the 18th Century, Russian hunters found and began to kill the otter on the shores of the Kamchatka Peninsula in Siberia. Its range then extended across the Bering Sea and the Aleutian Islands to Alaska and from there south as far as Baja California. When the first pelts reached the market in China and Russia, they were recognized as perhaps the most beautiful of all furs—superior even to sable—and remarkable prices were paid for them, $50 a skin on the average and, once, as much as $2,000 for a single skin. Glossy black to dark brown in color, the fur is about one and one half inches long when fluffed dry and it is astonishingly thick—on a large adult male there can be as many as 800 million hairs, according to one estimate.

Russian, Japanese, English and American hunters took an estimated one million pelts during a little more than a century and a half between the 1740s and 1911. By then the otter had been all but exterminated and the killing was finally stopped by international treaty. However, a few animals survived in remote enclaves and preserved the species, which is by no means endangered today. In Alaska, the population seems to be particularly healthy; the otter may never have disappeared in northern waters and its numbers have grown to about 120,000. But it was only in 1938 that the otter was resighted in California waters and began the geometric growth in population, the rapid expansion of range and the ruination of shellfish that have got it into trouble again.

It is difficult for anyone, except fishermen and their families, to frown on a sea otter. With most people, it is a case of anthropomorphic love at first sight. The creature belongs to the *Mustelidae* family of mammals, and although it is cousin to the weasel and the skunk, it has no objectionable scent glands. It is fairly big—a male may reach 65 inches in length, including its 10-inch tail, and weigh perhaps 85 pounds. It has catlike forepaws with retractable claws; webbed hind feet; bushy white whiskers reminiscent of the late Albert Schweitzer; and luminous, intelligent black eyes. It is mild and curious in temperament

and will swim up and gently accept food from the hands of naturalists or other gentle souls who might care to study it. It is born in the water and spends almost all its life (10 to 15 years) there, seldom coming ashore and rarely venturing more than a mile from land.

A CLEVER TOOL USER

By far, the sea otter's most remarkable quality is its use of stones, both as hammers and anvils, to separate shellfish from their underwater lodgments and then to break them open. In all of nature only man, the chimpanzee, the digger wasp, the Egyptian vulture, the Galapagos Islands finch and the blue jay—plus, of course, the sea otter—are known to use tools.

The otter's characteristic posture at dinner is Lucullan. It reclines on the water, floating on its back, a flat rock balanced on its chest. With loud whacks that can be heard more than half a mile away, it batters a clam against the rock until the shell is well cracked and the meat is exposed. After eating the clam, the otter fastidiously rolls or whirls in the water to wash away any loose fragments, then dives for more food. (It can reach depths of 180 feet and remain submerged for up to four minutes, but in California it prefers to forage in five to 40 feet of water and stays down for a minute or less.) On the bottom the otter snatches a second clam and selects another handy rock. It then rises to the surface with the rock tucked under one foreleg and the clam under the other. *Whack! Whack!* Naturalists have observed that the otter, though not so persistent as Lizzie Borden, will give a mollusk as many as 35 whacks before achieving the desired result.

The otter does not merely have expensive tastes. (Nice, fresh abalone sells in California markets for five dollars a pound.) The otter is also, of necessity, a glutton. Unlike other marine mammals—seals, porpoises, or whales—the sea otter does not have a protective layer of blubber. It does have a high metabolic rate and a body temperature of about 100°, and in order to keep from freezing in cold water it must rely on a prodigious intake of food, perhaps 25 per cent of its body weight every day.

In California waters a single adult male consumes more than three tons of food each year, a statistic that leaves fishermen in a state of open-mouthed shock. Abalones and sea urchins are its favorite meals, but the otter also devours Pismo, razor, gaper and littleneck clams; rock, red and kelp crabs; turban snails, mussels, scallops, barnacles, squid, octopus and occasional slow-moving fish.

In keeping warm, the otter must also rely on its remarkable fur. By making somersault-like turns on the surface of the water, it "blows" air into its fur and then distributes or traps it among the myriad hairs by frequent grooming or massage, thus providing insulation.

The otter's skin is loose—an animal that is a natural size 40, so to speak, has a size 42 or 44 skin so that it can move sections around to groom hard-to-reach areas. The loose skin is also helpful in providing pouch space for food. Otters often come to the surface carrying half a dozen small snails in a baggy fold.

Mother otters—gestation is thought to take eight or nine months, and as a rule only one pup is born—seem particularly fond parents. (The male not only ignores both pup and mother but occasionally steals food from them.) In a treatise published in 1868 one naturalist observed that the females, which clutch their young happily to their breasts, "caress and suckle their offspring seemingly with much affection, fondling them with their forepaws—reclining, in their usual manner—and frequently uttering a plaintive sound, which may have given rise to the saying that 'sea otters sing to quiet their young ones,' and gives some credence to the suggestion that the human-like actions of the animal originated the story about mermaids."

In the heyday of the fur trade, hunters took extremely cruel advantage of the otter's maternal affection. When they found a pup floating temporarily alone on the surface while its mother dove for food, the hunters would impale the pup on a hook and tow it screaming behind their boat. The mother, rising to defend it, was clubbed.

Otters frequently congregate in groups of 10 or more, known as rafts. They are gregarious, and in order to avoid being swept away from their companions by waves or tide while asleep, they drape an anchoring strand of bottom-rooted kelp around their midsections. In strong sunlight ot-

Buoyed up by the air trapped in their thick fur, these sea otters create a living raft by anchoring themselves together with long strands of kelp. Female otters often wrap their young in this floating seaweed while they forage for food.

ters have been observed sleeping with their fore-paws over their eyes; or when rising partway out of the water to peer at something in the distance, shading their eyes with a paw exactly as might a man with his hand.

POSING A PROBLEM FOR FISH AND GAME

However delightful a creature the otter may be, it was in 1975 a serious problem to the California State Department of Fish and Game. Among the citizenry there were organizations called Friends of the Sea Otter on one hand, and, for a time, Friends of the Abalone on the other. Who could wish to harm a sea otter? Contrariwise, who could wish to deprive a commercial fisherman of his livelihood, or a sport fisherman of his hard-earned relaxation?

As though this philosophical dilemma was not enough, the Department of Fish and Game found itself in an economic pinch as well. The department is supported almost entirely by fees from licenses—and as the otter worked toward elim-

Displaying an amazingly skillful use of tools, a sea otter breaks an abalone shell loose from the sea bottom with a stone. Its human competition, a commercial diver (right), uses a special tool to pry an abalone from a rock. If the tool slips, the abalone will immediately clamp down so hard on its rock that it cannot be pried loose.

inating the abalone and the clam, applications for licenses were falling off, limiting funds for essential work throughout the state.

No definitive solutions were in sight. The department was thinking of restricting the otters to the narrowest limits of their present 150-mile range, trapping individuals who strayed north or south of it. But if they were kept within a relatively narrow range they would be highly vulnerable to an oil spill, particularly after the big tankers start making their way south from the end of the new Alaskan pipeline *(pages 60-73)*.

And what could be done with the trapped strays? In earlier experiments, otters caught along the outer limits and released in the center had promptly returned to the periphery again, perhaps headed for the restaurants of Fisherman's Wharf in San Francisco. Could the excess otters be given to zoos and aquariums? They would make interesting gifts, to be sure: "All you have to do, sir, is give this fellow a flat rock and two and one half tons of clams a year."

Pipeline for a Wilderness

Working around the clock in one of the planet's coldest and wildest regions, the first of some 16,000 construction men began in April 1975 the most challenging engineering project since the Panama Canal: the $6 billion trans-Alaska pipeline. By mid-1977, it will bring 1.2 million barrels of crude oil each day from Prudhoe Bay on Alaska's barren North Slope to the ice-free port of Valdez, 800 miles south, to be transshipped to the "Lower 48" states.

Not that working around the clock means very much in the far North—daylight lasts nearly 24 hours in summer, while night spans as many hours in winter. The long nights of winter are only one of the obstacles in the way of the pipeline. It will have to be built across some of the most treacherous, and beautiful terrain on the globe, in one of the most difficult climates—temperatures along the route run from 70°F. at Valdez during the summer to —50°F. on the North Slope in winter, cold enough to freeze exposed human flesh in 30 seconds.

But the builders must not only overcome nature; they must preserve it. Preservation has proved to be a difficult and costly task. The biggest problem is the permafrost (map, page 63). Because oil will flow through the pipeline at 130°F., laying pipe on the ground, as is done in warmer climates, would be disastrous. The permafrost would melt, pipes would sag and break, and gushing oil would destroy feeding grounds of animals as small as lemmings and as large as caribou, sheep and bison. If these animals perished, species like the timber wolf, and the red fox on the opposite page, would be without a source of food. To prevent such ecological disruption, engineers devised three ways of laying pipe. Depending on the region, the line may be set above ground on stilts, simply buried or, oddly enough in frigid Alaska, refrigerated.

Seemingly unaware of the presence of man, a red fox peers from a snowy shelter of stacked culvert pipe, which will be used for constructing drains along the Alaska pipeline.

Space-Age Pipe for Frozen Earth

In planning the pipeline, engineers faced problems seldom met by oilmen: temperatures ranging from Florida warmth to arctic cold, which could distort and burst pipe; permafrost, which the warm oil in the pipe could melt; migrating animals, whose paths cross the route; and even earth tremors. Imaginative solutions were required, and the engineers supplied them.

Pipe was constructed of vanadium steel, an alloy flexible enough to withstand severe stresses. In areas where permafrost may melt, the pipeline is raised. The pipeline is buried where there is no permafrost, or where it consists of a rocky aggregate. In permafrost areas where migrations are heavy and animals might avoid raised pipe, it is buried (to permit animal passage) and refrigerated (to prevent permafrost thaws). In earthquake zones, the line will be raised and clamped to special "shoes" that slide as much as 25 feet sideways. Finally the supports for raised pipe will be refrigerated to make sure heat is never communicated to the permafrost.

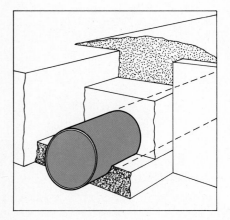
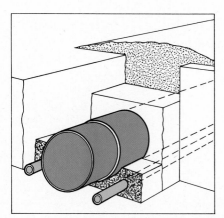

The pipeline will be buried in gravel (left) along 409 miles where the permafrost is solid enough to prevent warm oil in the pipes from melting it. The pipe rests on a gravel bed, is surrounded with a gravel cushion and is topped off with a "crown" of earth. Some pipe must be buried in easily melted permafrost; in that case (right) smaller pipes carrying a refrigerated brine solution will flank each pipe segment in the gravel bed.

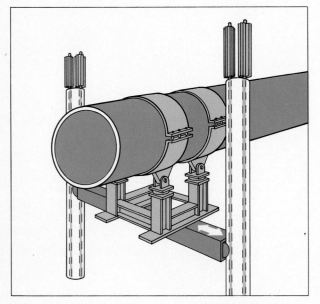
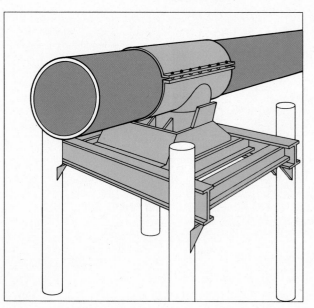

For most of the 382 miles where the permafrost is not solid enough for buried pipe, it is raised on earthquake shock absorbers. Every 50-to-70 feet is a sliding shoe, attached to a crossbeam. The shoe can move laterally (arrow), compensating for shifts caused by earth tremors. Since heat from the pipe could flow down the supports and thaw the permafrost, each support will contain pipes (dotted lines) filled with a refrigerant that draws heat from the supports and expels it through radiators on their tops.

At intervals of 800 to 1,800 feet, raised pipeline will be bolted to rigid crossbars attached to four upright supports. These anchor points limit pipe movement on the shock-absorbing shoes (left). Not shown is a four-inch layer of heat-insulating fiberglass that will sheathe all raised pipe and will in turn be covered with galvanized steel to keep the fiberglass from flaking off. Engineers feel that the insulation, along with the other safeguards, will keep heat produced by oil in the pipeline away from the ground.

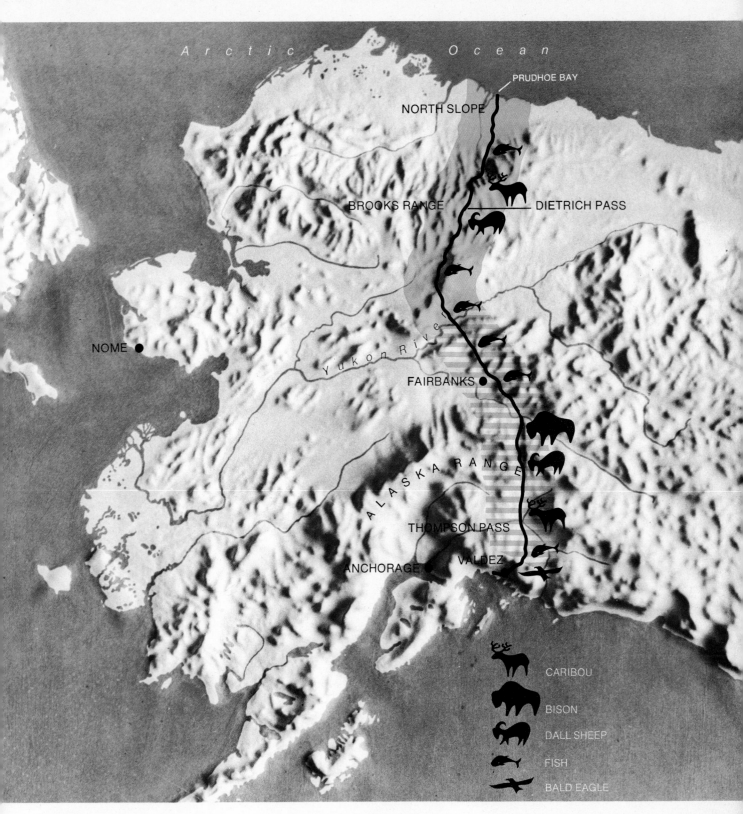

ARCTIC Ocean

PRUDHOE BAY

NORTH SLOPE

BROOKS RANGE — DIETRICH PASS

Yukon River

NOME

FAIRBANKS

ALASKA RANGE

THOMPSON PASS

ANCHORAGE   VALDEZ

CARIBOU

BISON

DALL SHEEP

FISH

BALD EAGLE

The 800-mile-long Alaska pipeline will start at Prudhoe Bay on the North Slope, snake south for 150 miles across a flat arctic desert, climb 4,800 feet over the Dietrich Pass in the Brooks Range, plunge down to cross the broad Yukon River—the largest of 70 rivers along the pipeline's path —climb 3,300 feet over the Alaska Range, and then cross Thompson Pass in the Chugach Mountains before finally arriving at the ice-free port of Valdez. While the terrain the pipeline traverses is rugged, it is not always stable. Permafrost is continuous for more than 350 miles (red) and is intermittent (red and white) for about 400 miles. Because the pipeline might disturb wildlife habitats (key), special building techniques are being used and construction schedules are planned so as not to interfere with them. A particular problem was the 450,000 caribou that each year migrate across what will be the pipeline's route. At these wildlife crossing points, buried and refrigerated pipe is being laid.

Each spring and fall caribou like these race over the tundra, migrating across the pipeline path.

◄ Two timber wolves meander down the gravel road used to carry supplies to a construction camp near Prudhoe.

A grizzly bear sniffs out a trail in the ► Alaska Range, one of the rugged regions the 800-mile pipeline will cross.

While its companions watch, a Dall sheep munches on an alpine flower pulled from the rich tundra.

Protecting a Priceless Resource

Alaska is one of the largest wildlife areas in North America, a unique refuge that is home to hundreds of species now rare in more southerly regions. Since the 800-mile-long pipeline will cross paths with many of these animals, unusual steps have been taken to protect them. The pipeline will be buried as deep as nine feet at three points near the Copper River so that caribou can migrate without hindrance. Where construction might silt up rivers and harm fish, special basins will be built to trap debris. At river crossings, pipe will be carried on special bridges or buried under their beds, so that warm oil in the pipe will not raise water temperatures and kill fish.

Not the least of the threats to wildlife is the men doing the work. Accordingly, hunting and fishing will be banned in a five-mile-wide corridor along the pipeline, and where salmon spawn or Dall sheep lamb, work will stop until the animals finish doing what comes naturally.

Tools and Techniques for a Frigid Job

Laying the 102,000 48-inch-diameter segments of the trans-Alaska pipeline—and hauling parts for its 12 gas-turbine pumping stations—is a task demanding not only an army of skilled workers but a battery of newfangled techniques. Welders ride in heated rigs that move on top of oil pipe, thus protecting both worker and weld from the elements. Because water would freeze as it came out a nozzle, steam hoses are used to wash down equipment.

The trickiest part of the job, however, remains the permafrost. Just scratching its surface leaves scars that melt and deepen until they bog down equipment. Thus, when heavy vehicles move over permafrost they must do so on enormous tires that are so soft that they leave the thin cover of vegetation unbroken.

A worker's face mask is encrusted with his frozen breath after a 10-hour shift on the oil fields of the North Slope, where winter temperatures average a numbing —50° F.

Brightly painted earthmovers inch through the snowy Brooks Range, bound for the major construction site on Alaska's Prudhoe Bay, 300 miles inside the Arctic Circle.

Working from a barge in the Yukon River, construction men race the approaching freeze-up to complete pylons for a 2,295-foot bridge to carry the pipe across the river.

An earthmover dumps gravel into a waiting truck on the North Slope. Engines will be kept running day and night to prevent oil and battery fluid from freezing.

His face shield glowing eerily in the dark of Arctic winter, a welder works on a 60-foot-long pipeline support, one of 80,000 such structures that will be buried in the permafrost.

Roughing It in Arctic Luxury

In sharp contrast to the often brutal harshness of the weather and terrain in which the crews work is their comfort after hours. The 16,000 men and 1,500 women toiling on the huge job for a consortium of eight oil companies can relax in un-Arctic luxury. Camps along the pipeline offer hearty meals of steak, roast beef and fresh vegetables; after dinner there are movies and taped TV programs. The workers (who put in a seven-day week and get one week in 10 off) can take added comfort from a pay range of $1,500 a week for skilled workers to $700 for dishwashers.

At the pipeline terminal on Prudhoe Bay, two permanent establishments have been set up by Atlantic Richfield and British Petroleum for workers who will stay to drill for oil after the pipeline is completed. British Petroleum's spread is by far the most sumptuous: Its $21-million building *(above)* includes a game room with pool tables, a heated swimming pool and even a sauna.

British Petroleum's prefabricated living quarters glow in the dark like a beached cruise ship. The dormitory building is constructed on stilts not only to lift it above drifting snow but also to keep its heat away from the permafrost.

Workers at Galbraith Construction Camp, 140 miles south of Prudhoe Bay, eat abundantly. During peak construction periods along the pipeline, workers will consume 32 tons of food, flown in each day.

Dubbed "Prudhoe National Forest" by workers, these spruce and birch trees are the only ones on the North Slope. They were planted in a glass enclosure and provide a view for the dining hall in the British Petroleum living quarters.

71

The snow-buried promontories of the Chugach Mountains loom frigidly behind Valdez's Prince William Sound, chosen as terminus of the Alaska pipeline because it remains ice-free all year round. Three supertankers will be able to put into Valdez each day to pick up more than a million barrels of oil destined for refineries on the West Coast of the ''Lower 48.''

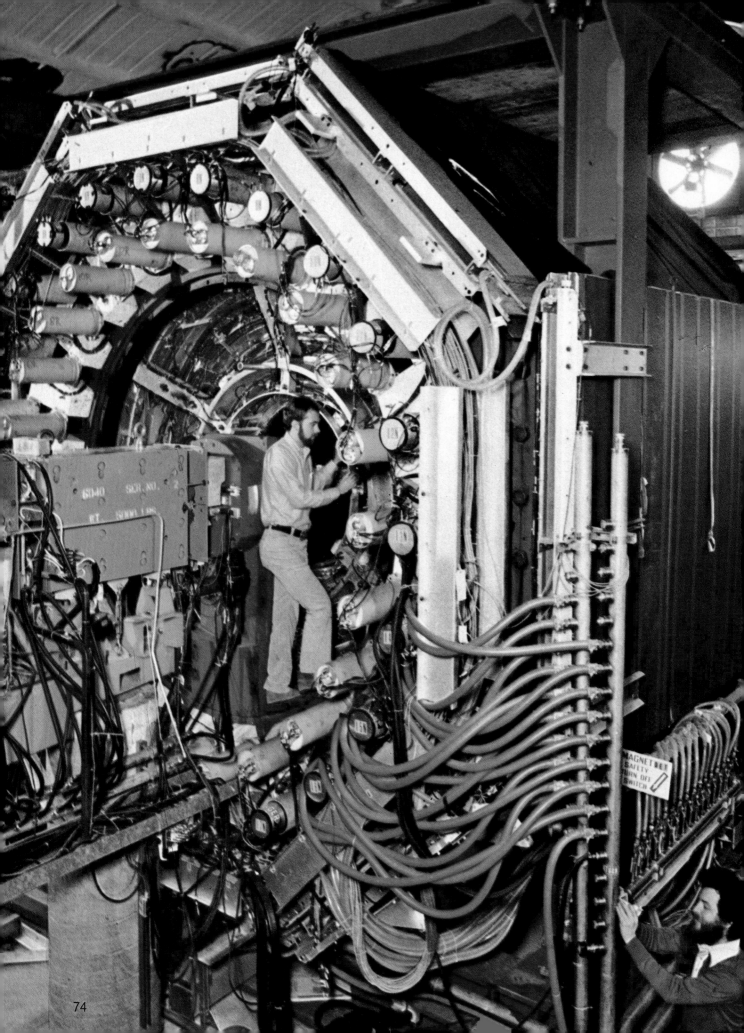

The Mysterious Psi

IS IT THE LONG-SOUGHT KEY TO THE RIDDLE OF MATTER?

by C. P. Gilmore

At eight o'clock on the morning of Monday, November 11, 1974, Samuel C. C. Ting of M.I.T., on the West Coast for a meeting of physicists, walked into the office of Burton Richter at Stanford University.

"Burt, I've got some very exciting physics to tell you," said Ting.

"*I've* got some exciting physics to tell *you,*" interrupted Richter.

The news that each man had to tell the other was the same. Two experimental teams, working a continent apart, performing different kinds of experiments with different kinds of equipment, had simultaneously made a discovery that could change basic ideas about the fundamental nature of matter.

Each had discovered the same new particle, an evanescent speck of material inside the more substantial specks that make up the atoms that make up the things of the world. But it was not just another routine particle to add to the already well-populated array that scientists call the "nuclear zoo." It was an incredible particle that has since been hailed as a landmark in the history of physics. Victor Weisskopf of M.I.T., one of the country's leading theoretical physicists, says, "They have discovered some new way nature behaves, and we don't understand why." Adds Ting, "A large amount of theory will have to be changed to explain this."

For more than 50 years physicists have been penetrating into ever-deeper layers of matter and

Surrounded by the complicated mechanisms of a particle detector at the Stanford Linear Accelerator Center, two physicists make adjustments. The scientist at top works on the atom smasher's detection equipment. The large gray box behind him is a magnet that focuses a beam of particles into the center of the octagon-shaped detector, where it smashes into another beam from the opposite direction. The man at the lower right is checking the pressure system on the tubes that carry water for cooling the magnet.

Members of one team of psi particle discoverers—left
to right, Martin Perl, Burton Richter and Gerson Goldhaber
—discuss their mysterious find at the Stanford Linear
Accelerator Center, a short distance south of San Francisco.
Behind the three physicists is an oscilloscope screen,
displaying the tracks left by the particle (detail at right).

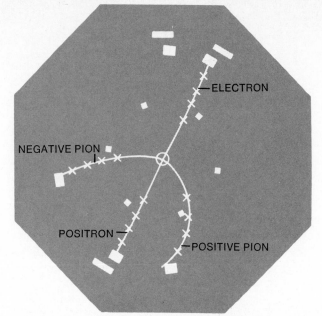

Though the psi particle cannot be seen, it leaves tracks
—which by coincidence look like the Greek letter psi
—when it "decays." It first generates particles called pions
(curved lines) and another psi of lower energy. The new
psi decays into a negative electron and a positive positron.
The X-marks are computer measures of the decay tracks.

energy in the attempt to answer the ultimate
questions: What is matter? Why is the universe
the way it is?

Evidence from thousands of experiments has
been pieced together bit by bit and an elaborate
theoretical framework has been constructed to
contain it. Now, suddenly, from the collision between particles accelerated to nearly the speed
of light and then smashed together has popped
a strange bit of matter that threatens to bring
down the fragile house of theory constructed at
great cost over the decades. Or it could do the reverse. When the meaning of the new particle is
understood, it may turn out to embody some now
unknown physical law that will bring presently
hazy areas into sharp focus and thus greatly improve our understanding of the universe. It could
even help physicists extract from the subatomic
world the simplicity and order they have always
been sure is lurking there.

Simultaneous discovery of a new particle is
not unprecedented in physics, not even unusual;
but rarely in this fiercely competitive science

has there been such a dead heat as this one.

The momentous find was made with the use of
two of the largest pieces of the physicist's
artillery: the Alternating Gradient Synchrotron
(AGS) at the Brookhaven National Laboratory on
New York's Long Island and the Stanford Linear
Accelerator Center (SLAC) at Stanford University
a few miles south of San Francisco. These two
giant multimillion-dollar atom smashers—or accelerators, as the physicists call them—work in
quite different ways. Seen from the air, the AGS
is like a circular racetrack, one half mile in circumference. It is covered entirely with earth to
contain the radiation that is released by the reactions within. Across the country, on the West
Coast, SLAC is easily recognizable from the air
as a two-mile-long building with a Y-shaped cluster of structures at one end.

In each case, a beam of subatomic particles is
either hurled down a long straight path (as at
SLAC) or accelerated around and around (as at
Brookhaven) until the particles are moving within a fraction of a per cent of the velocity of light

and are charged with an energy of billions of electron volts—enough power to light several city blocks. Once energized, the subatomic particles are smashed into a stationary target or into one another while instruments record what fragments are produced by the collisions.

ONE INTERESTING REACTION AMONG BILLIONS

Using the AGS, a group of 30 physicists from 10 countries, under the direction of Ting, had begun using this standard technique in a systematic search for very rare particles formed in the collisions. These sought-after reactions occur so seldom that a lot of reactions have to be produced to get even a few desired ones. In this case Ting was using a beam of protons—one of the two large composite units of the nucleus of an atom—providing about one trillion protons per second. He and his team had spent 10 years in building the exceedingly complex computer-controlled detectors that could single out the interesting reactions from the billions of others going on—and do so in a billionth of a second.

To protect the experimenters from the radiation generated when particles are destroyed and created in the pulsing reactions, the detectors are shielded even more massively than the circular accelerator: They are buried under 10,000 tons of concrete, five tons of uranium, which is an excellent shielding agent because of its tremendous density, and five tons of borax soap, containing the element boron which absorbs particularly harmful nuclear particles. At least 18 physicists, six to a shift, three shifts around the clock, operate the detectors and collect data for weeks or months at a time.

This enormous effort first showed signs of paying off in a big way in August 1974, when the experimenters began detecting large numbers of paired electrons and positrons. Positrons are identical to electrons except that they have a positive rather than a negative electric charge. When found paired with electrons, they indicate the end result of the disintegration of some larger particle. The combined energy of the pair indicates the parent particle's size, since mass is interchangeable with energy in physics. The combined energy of the electron-positron pairs

At Brookhaven National Laboratory, Samuel Ting holds a printout of data on the particle he found and named J —identical to psi but discovered several months earlier.

detected by Ting's team was 3.112 billion electron volts. No particle of that mass had ever been discovered. But it would have profound effects on the entire field of physics if it turned out that it was real.

Ting decided to check carefully before announcing his results to the world of physics. From August to September the group checked and rechecked, recalibrated the machine and operated it at other power settings. The abundance of the pairs did not change. The discovery was real. Ting named the particle J, using a standard physics notation system, and prepared to publish a paper that he knew would cause a sensation in the physics community.

Meanwhile, the West Coast research team under Richter's leadership was working along a quite different tack. They were not breaking up protons to see what sort of electron-positron pairs teamed up in the debris. Instead, they started out with electrons and positrons, smashing them together in the hope of finding something new in the aftermath of the collisions. High-energy electrons, first accelerated to nearly the speed of light down the length of the two-mile-long linear accelerator at Stanford, were then switched into a "storage ring," where they were kept circulating in one direction. A beam of positrons was put into the ring circulating in the other direction. The two beams collided head on, the particles annihilating one another and producing showers of secondary particles. Huge magnets and detecting chambers surrounding the experimental area detected and measured the results of these energetic reactions.

It was this enormously large, complex and expensive piece of scientific apparatus that Richter's group set out to work with in the spring of 1972. They were investigating what happened in electron-positron collisions between energies of 2.6 to 5 billion electron volts, a largely unexplored range. Such experiments take a lot of time. Although billions of electrons and positrons are flying around the ring, they are very small and seldom score a direct hit on one another. So it may take many hours—perhaps 30 in a typical experiment—to make a single accurate measurement at one energy level. If 300 hours are set aside for one experiment—a lot in view of the fierce competition for machine time—then measurements can be taken at a dozen different points in the target range.

A VERY SUSPICIOUS BUMP

The first results were puzzling. When they were plotted on a graph showing results at various energy levels, a peculiar bump in the curve showed up at 3.2 billion electron volts. In June 1974, the machine was shut down for modifications. When it started up again in October, Richter had decided to investigate the suspicious area more closely. The first measurement was at 3.3 billion, and nothing unusual was noted. But when the equipment was switched to 3.1 billion, several of the readings showed wild excursions from normal. As one observer put it, "When you get a crazy reading, there are two possibilities. Either the equipment is acting up (common), or the physics is acting up (rare)." So the experimenters began looking for equipment problems.

The storage rings were still being tuned and refined during the week, so Richter's people were using it on weekends. On Saturday, November 9, having uncovered nothing wrong with the equipment, they began taking measurements again at 3.1 billion electron volts. Throughout the night, the experimenters continued to ease the power levels up through small steps: 3.100, 3.101, 3.102. By 11 o'clock Sunday morning, they had charted a new island of knowledge in the sea of physics. At levels near 3.105 billion electron volts, one set of readings suddenly shot a hundred times higher than they had been. The meaning was clear to the physicists: In the seething collisions within the machine, particles were being created out of energy at a high rate. Because matter and energy are interchangeable, the mass of the particle being made could be calculated with Einstein's famous formula, $E = mc^2$. And the mass was like no other particle ever before seen.

Even odder was its lifetime. Physicists know that very few subatomic particles last very long (those few form the material world of ordinary experience). Most of the hundreds of others that have been discovered in atom smashers disappear in periods of time that are too short to seem to have meaning in the real world. Most of the subatomic particles exist for no longer than .000000000000000000000001 second. But these particles were extraordinarily long-lived: some .000000000000000000001 second, or 1,000 times longer than might have been expected. In the time scale established by the flow of events in human affairs, the difference would not seem to be important. But the factor of a thousand was, to physicists, astonishing. It was as though a zoologist accustomed to studying a variety of insects that normally live a month ran upon a similar strain that lived as long as man—70 years. He would instantly assume he had stumbled not only onto some incredible new and unknown law of nature that was producing the weird effect he had seen, but also onto a principle that could have profound meaning for the entire field. The mysterious particle had the same potential. Because it did not fit the pattern, it might be saying something new about nature. If so, it was essential to find out what.

At 11 a.m. the first bottle of champagne was opened and, while most team members stood around in a state of euphoria congratulating one another, one member, Gerson Goldhaber, found a quiet office and began writing a report to inform the scientific community of the discovery. The Stanford team used a Greek letter to name the newly found particle, continuing another scientific tradition for the identification of particles. They called it psi.

While the history-making experiments at Stanford were still going on, Ting was boarding his plane in New York to attend the long-planned physicists' meeting set for Monday morning. And it was less than 24 hours after the moment of excitement that he entered Richter's office with his desire to "tell some exciting physics."

On the morning of November 11, as Ting and Richter sat exchanging data, it became clear that J and psi were indeed the same particle. (Ting's discovery had come in August—three months before Richter's. But Ting is known as a meticulous worker, and he elected to recheck before saying anything. Had he not been so cautious, he could have published in early fall and got full credit for the discovery.)

Virtually no business that the meeting had originally been called to deal with got done as the men brought their colleagues up to date on the new work. Within hours, word had reached Europe by phone, and already the giant accelerators in Italy and Germany were being readied to repeat the experiment and confirm its validity (which they did within days). Ten days later, at 4:30 on the morning of November 21, Richter discovered a second mysterious particle at 3.7 billion electron volts. It had many of the same characteristics of the first and clearly belonged to the same family. It was called psi 3700.

The discovery of the psi particle is the latest —but surely not the last—step in the search for the heart of matter. As far back as 400 B.C., the philosopher Democritus proposed that matter, though incredibly diverse, must be made from indestructible bits he named atoms. Isaac Newton agreed, writing, "It seems probable to me that God in the beginning formed Matter in solid, massy, hard, impenetrable, moveable Particles."

By the 1930s it seemed that Democritus and Newton were essentially correct. All the world had been shown to be made up of atoms, and atoms were apparently made of only three distinct particles: lightweight, negatively charged electrons; heavy, positively charged protons; and heavy, electrically uncharged neutrons. In addition, it had been discovered that light was not simply wave energy as had been thought, but at times seemed to behave like a string of particles. The light particle was called a photon. These ideas accounted for almost all characteristics of matter—almost, but not all.

THE STRANGE COMPLEXITY OF NATURE

The attempt to clear up the few remaining details was to plunge physics into a series of crises and replace the illusion of simplicity with levels of incredible complexity just now being sorted out. As physicists continued to explore the subatomic world, additional particles were discovered—not just a few but hundreds. "Can nature really be so complicated?" mused one writer in 1948. "May it not be that some, at least, of these particles are compounds of even more elementary building blocks?"

The strange new particles that had started to emerge from the atomic nucleus in swarms 25 years ago all had one remarkable thing in common. They were all very short-lived, unlike the electrons, protons and neutrons of ordinary matter, and rapidly "decayed" into other particles. They changed into various forms until they reached stable states such as the electron and proton, giving off photons in the form of light, X-rays, or X-ray-like gamma rays as they went.

After many years of observation, this decay process was seen to obey a complex set of rules. A particle could decay into one particle but not into another because certain conservation laws were being followed. These laws resemble the ordinary natural laws of conservation—neither matter nor energy can be destroyed—but they relate to conservation of electric charge, angular momentum (the energy of spin in a rotating particle), or other, more unusual qualities. A strange fact was discovered about these conserved characteristics: Electric charge, for example, always occurs in multiples of the basic charge of the electron, +1, +2, +3, −1, −2, etc., never in a fraction of the basic charge. The other qualities behave similarly; they occur in no numbers that are not multiples of the basic quantity. These numbers are called quantum numbers.

Once a system of quantum numbers has been devised, a chart can be made of all possible reactions; the physicists can predict, in other words, what nature should be making if the theory is correct. By applying a kind of algebra given by the quantum numbers, science could make a great many predictions about what particles would or would not do.

While some sense could be made out of the proliferating particles by such methods, it remained in the late 1950s for a brash young physicist named Murray Gell-Mann to come up with an important new idea. Gell-Mann was a certifiable child prodigy. He entered Yale at 15 and got his Ph.D. from M.I.T. at 21. At 24, puzzling on the strange behavior of 10 particles that lived millions of times longer than they should have by then-current theory, he decided that a new quantum number was involved. He whimsically named it "strangeness."

Strangeness—unlike qualities such as charge and spin—does not have any meaning that can be described. But analysis of the particle-decay patterns that the conservation laws permit leads to logical interrelationships between them. A particle with a strangeness of 2 can decay into another with a strangeness of 2, or into any combination of particles that add up to 2. But it cannot decay into a particle with a strangeness of 3 because a conservation law would be violated. Strangeness turned out to be the key that unlocked the secret of the odd behavior of the particles and allowed physicists to predict what would happen in many mysterious reactions.

Shortly after Gell-Mann invented the concept of strangeness, James D. Bjorken and Sheldon Lee Glashow at the Bohr Institute in Copenhagen devised another quantum number that may, although no one could predict it at the time, help to explain psis. Bjorken and Glashow were troubled by an inexplicable irregularity in certain reactions, and they hypothesized that if there

were another quantum number, the reactions would be regularized. The quality was called charm ("I don't know why they give them names like that," says M.I.T.'s Victor Weisskopf. "That's psychology, not physics.") Six years later, several Harvard physicists were trying to figure out why certain reactions that should occur did not. The same hypothetical charm, their calculations showed, could explain the mystery. The reactions did not occur because charm would not be conserved if they did.

But while there was progress toward understanding the behavior of the countless particles that seemed to inhabit the atom, the big questions remained: Why were there so many? How did they relate to one another? In 1961 Gell-Mann (and, independently, an Israeli colonel named Yuval Ne'eman) invented a classification scheme that Gell-Mann called the Eightfold Way, referring, playfully as always, to an aphorism about the tenets of right living attributed to Buddha: "Now this, O monks, is noble truth that leads to the cessation of pain: This is the noble Eightfold Way." Gell-Mann's Eightfold Way classified particles into families of eight or 10. Just how much it led to the cessation of pain on the part of physicists is hard to say, but it made some sense of the confusing plethora of particles by putting them in a logical-looking pattern.

THE HUNT FOR THE BASIC PARTICLE

Still, the search for the "fundamental" particle (physicists always put the word in quotes) was as bogged down as ever. Certainly not all of these particles were fundamental; many of them, in fact, were clearly made from each other. Was anything fundamental?

Gell-Mann then went on to a bold idea (almost simultaneously with George Zweig, his colleague at Caltech). No fractional electric charge had ever been seen; electric charge always came in packages that were multiples of the charge on the electron. But Gell-Mann hypothesized that the truly fundamental particle might have a fractional charge, which, still whimsical, he named the quark from the line in James Joyce, "Three quarks for Muster Mark."

Postulating three kinds of quarks, Gell-Mann

On the Track of Einstein's Grand Scheme

Almost to the day he died in 1955, the great theoretical physicist Albert Einstein was involved in a vain struggle to produce a unified field theory—a grand scheme of equations to interrelate four seemingly diverse forces that are believed to determine the behavior of all matter. Two of these forces are known to everyone—gravity, which causes objects to fall toward Earth, and electromagnetism, which drives electric motors. The other two are more esoteric: the strong force, which binds together the nuclei of atoms; and the weak force, which causes certain atoms to disintegrate into others.

For years after Einstein's death, these forces seemed completely disconnected and dissimilar. Then in 1973, an international team of physicists startled the scientific community by announcing that they might have found a link between two of these forces. Each force is embodied in particles of subatomic matter—the energy of a force is, after all, interchangeable with an equivalent mass of matter. Particles representing the electromagnetic and weak forces turned out to behave alike.

Physicists had known that when particles associated with the electromagnetic force—either electrons or their oppositely charged duplicates, positrons—collide with certain other particles, the resulting fragments have the same electric charge as the original particles, indicating that no charge is transferred in the reaction. When a similar experiment was conducted using neutrinos—the chargeless, massless particles associated with the weak force—the neutrinos reacted the way electromagnetic force positrons or electrons did. What emerged from the collision was apparently more chargeless, massless neutrinos. The similarity of the reactions led the physicists to conclude that electromagnetic and weak forces may indeed be linked, as had been predicted by Harvard's Steven Weinberg—a first step toward proof of the interrelationship of states of matter so long sought by Einstein.

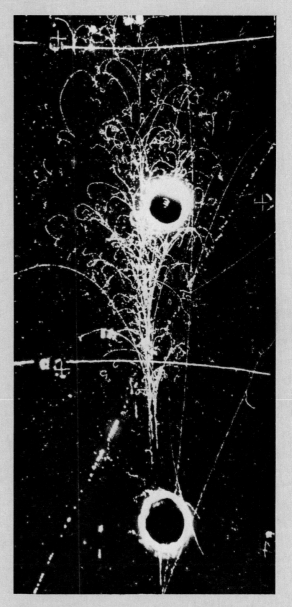

The tracks above, recording a collision of a strange particle called a neutrino with other subatomic matter, provide the first evidence supporting a theory linking two universal forces. The only charged particles detected were electrons (long curved track at left) and pions (vertical track in center). Another particle had to be produced, and the absence of any track indicates that, as the theory predicted, it was an uncharged neutrino, which leaves no track.

demonstrated that combinations of them and their mirror images, or anti-quarks, would account for all properties of all known particles. Even more important, it was clear that some particles that had not yet been detected should also be possible. And in 1964 the quark theory scored an important triumph (and Gell-Mann clinched the Nobel Prize) when the celebrated omega-minus particle, predicted on the basis of quark theory, was actually found.

While there have been problems in fitting all observed facts into the quark model, overall it has worked well. There is, however, one troubling fact. Despite Herculean attempts by experimental physicists, nobody has detected a quark. If quarks reside inside the proton and neutron, then they are very tightly bound indeed. Perhaps higher-energy accelerators would shake one loose. Perhaps quarks obey a strange law that makes it impossible ever to get them out. Perhaps—and Gell-Mann himself put forth this theory—they are not real entities at all, but simply mathematical inventions that make the esoteric world of particle physics easier to deal with.

A CRITICAL EXPERIMENT

And that is where things stood in late 1972, when a crucial experiment began at the same Stanford linear accelerator where the psi would later be discovered. The experiment was important not only because of its unexpected findings, but also because it illustrates so clearly the basic nature of scientific progress: It results not from the single compelling experiment, no matter how cleverly conceived or beautifully done, but from a painstaking and at times frustratingly slow approach to truth. The scientist looks at nature and makes a theory, speculating what the fundamental principles must be to produce such a result. Then he devises an experiment to investigate the theory or to test its predictive ability. If he obtains unexpected results—and this is not an unusual occurrence—then the theory may have to be modified or thrown out altogether. Thus the road to scientific understanding is traveled a laborious step at a time.

The SLAC experiment in 1972 was an attempt to test a certain prediction of the quark theory.

Implicit in this theory is the production of a fixed ratio of certain particles during a certain reaction. Yet in the SLAC experiment, the ratio changed sharply and the numbers obtained were outside the theoretical limits. Quarks were in trouble. The theory either had to be thrown out or had to be modified to be consistent with the new experimental evidence. After some stewing, physicists worked out a slight variation of the theory by adding one additional quark to the original three. And, calculations showed, the fix would work only if the fourth quark had that previously hypothesized quality: charm.

But as attractive as the idea of rescuing the quark theory with charm seemed, there was one nagging aspect: Charm was entirely theoretical. There was no hard evidence that it existed.

It was into this uneasy scene that the discovery of the psi burst, last fall, like fireworks. At first it seemed to make no sense because of its great mass and astonishingly long life. "The theoreticians are running for cover," said one experimenter. Meanwhile, the big accelerators around the world concentrated on psi, trying to discover its properties, what brothers and sisters it might have, and why it behaves as it does.

Results of the complex and costly experiments led to a rash of theories. One of them postulates that another hypothetical quantum number, called color, must be invoked to explain the psi's strange behavior. This would involve three quarks, each of which could come in three colors for a total of nine quarks altogether. Yet another theory would imbue psi with a quality called gentleness, and all matter would be made of three ordinary quarks and three gentle ones. (These names, despite their whimsy, do not represent simply vague schemes. Each is the result of a complex mathematical analysis that makes far-reaching numerical predictions about particle behavior. The names are then tacked on to identify the particular math scheme involved.)

Martin B. Einhorn and Chris Quigg of the Fermi National Accelerator Laboratory in Batavia, Illinois, have proposed a quantum number, which they call panda. This name would be appropriate, they believe, "because of the panda's well-known shyness and tendency to stay among his own kind." And, of course, it would mean that the new substance expressing the quality could be called pandamonium, a reasonably fair description of the state of physics brought on by the discovery of psi.

So the genteel banter continues in the arcane journals through which physicists communicate. While no one is now brave enough—or foolhardy enough—to make definite predictions, one theory clearly leads the rest. It was one of the first made. It hypothesized that the psi particle might be made of a quark and an antiquark, both with the property of charm. (The psi, then, could be said to be a bit of charmonium.)

If this hypothesis is true, the psi will be the first experimental evidence that charm is real.

Charm may rescue the faltering quark theory. And quark theory is still far and away the best bet to penetrate the ultimately simple scheme that physicists are convinced lies at the heart of nature. At least some physicists are—but not all. "I believe," says Victor Weisskopf, "that nature is inexhaustible and one will never find the final equation. The deeper you go, the more you find. And that is perhaps the beauty of nature."

But whether there is any end or not, the mystery that lures physicists out on the lonely brink of discovery is irresistible. "The universe is not only queerer than we suppose," said the British scientist J.B.S. Haldane, "but queerer than we *can* suppose." And where mystery exists, the human mind cannot rest.

The heart of the world's largest particle accelerator is this main ring tunnel, four miles in circumference. Its boxlike electromagnets enclose a vacuum chamber through which atom-smashing particles travel at nearly the speed of light. The blue magnets bend the beam of particles to keep it moving smoothly around the ring; orange ones (center) keep the beam focused in the center of the vacuum tube. The silver pipes hold water to cool the magnets, which are heated to around 100° F. by the strong current required to magnetize them. The rectangular pipe at top contains electronic instrument cables. The accelerator is a part of the Fermi National Accelerator Laboratory in Batavia, Illinois.

Next Stop: The Planet Mars

If the plans work out, the United States will be given a significant—and scientifically gratifying—present for its 200th birthday: a landing on Mars. There, close to the Fourth of July 1976, the first of two robots is scheduled to touch down, look around with camera eyes, reach out to pick up things, then sniff, bake and test them in the hope, finally, of answering the age-old question of whether there is life on the Red Planet.

A partial answer was supplied in 1972, when an unmanned spacecraft called Mariner 9 orbited Mars and beamed back to Earth photographs that revealed a planet with amazingly Earth-like features. There were mammoth canyons, what appeared to be riverbeds, volcanoes, ice caps and even clouds of water vapor *(Nature/Science Annual 1973, Remaking the Map of Mars, pages 62-71)*. From Mariner's photographs, four promising landing sites *(pages 88-89)* were selected for an attempt, scheduled for launch in the summer of 1975, to find Martian life—if any exists.

The Viking mission will launch two vehicles designed to place two robot explorers on Mars. Each Lander will have two cameras to send back pictures of large-scale life—what noted astronomer Carl Sagan calls "macrobes"—and laboratories to test Martian soil for the presence of microbes. The $1 billion mission—seven years in preparation—required the talents of 5,000 scientists and engineers.

Once launched by their two 159-foot-tall Titan III/Centaur rockets, the Viking spacecraft will cruise 11 months, then swing into an orbit around Mars. Instruments on the Orbiter will scan landing sites for obstructions or sandstorms that could abort landings, and also attempt to detect warm and wet spots within the sites where life would be most likely. Then the two parts of each craft will separate. The Orbiters will continue to circle Mars while the Landers will plunge through Mars' thin air, settle gently on its surface and begin the hunt for Martians.

Workmen at the White Sands Test Facility attach shrouds to a heat shield, needed to protect the Mars Lander when it plunges through the planet's atmosphere. The shield was repeatedly lifted by balloon to 120,000 feet to test its braking parachute—which successfully deployed.

Multiple Maneuvers to Reach a Far-off Planet

The Centaur stage ignites briefly (left), jettisoning the Titan stage two and setting the craft into temporary Earth orbit. A blast gives a push toward Mars and the Orbiter-Lander is ejected (above), solar panels extended, and the protective cap is discarded. After the spacecraft coasts 460 million miles, rockets turn it (above, right), so when the engine fires, it enters a Mars orbit.

Some 150,000 feet above Earth, Titan's second stage fires as the first stage is jettisoned, and shrouds protecting the Centaur stage drop away.

The Titan III/Centaur launch vehicle, lifting away from Earth, is powered by solid fuel boosters, which are discarded as Titan's main engines fire.

The complexity of the Mars mission is illustrated by this sequential drawing, which shows a Viking's metamorphosis from streamlined launch vehicle to spidery Mars Lander. The most difficult portion of this 11-month, 460 million-mile voyage will come when the Lander, separated from its parent ship, the Orbiter, begins its descent through Mars' atmosphere.

Because the Lander will then be so far from Earth, commands beamed to the craft will take a painfully long 20 minutes to reach it. To avoid delays in controlling the craft during the landing sequence shown at lower right, a preprogramed computer aboard the Lander will take command, deploying the parachute and firing braking rockets to enable the Lander to settle softly on Mars.

After thoroughly checking its Mars landing sites with cameras and infrared instruments, the Orbiter ejects the Lander in a clamshell capsule (above). While the Orbiter (above, right) discards the base that held the Lander in place and continues to circle Mars, the capsule rockets fire to pull it out of orbit (right) and send it down to land.

At 21,000 feet above Mars' surface, a 58-foot parachute deploys and the Lander heat shield falls away. At 4,000 feet, the legs are extended into position and three braking rockets fire.

Six to 13 minutes after its entering the Martian atmosphere, the Lander is down, and one of its two stack-shaped cameras begins to scan the surface for any signs of life. Then the long soil scoop, working like an elephant's trunk, digs its samples from the Red Planet's soil in order to search for microscopic plants and animals.

Picking a Haven in Unknown Territory

Long before the Viking craft were launched toward Mars, scientists had begun the crucial task of selecting landing sites that were safe and seemed likely to contain life. (There had been fears that the Landers would smash themselves

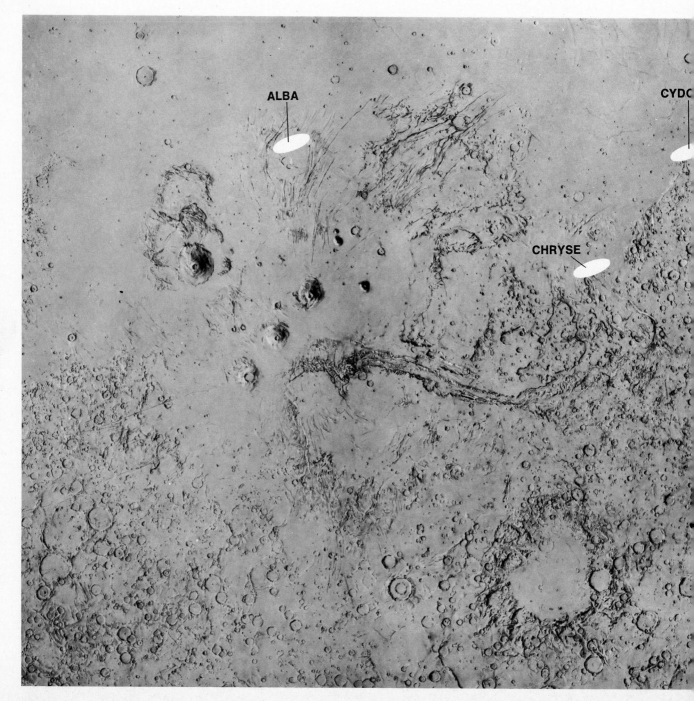

on rough terrain or sink up to their delicate sensors in Martian dust.) The places finally chosen, shown as 50-by-150-mile ellipses on the map below, all have one thing in common: they are situated where there might be water. One target, Chryse, is on a plain at the mouth of a gigantic canyon. The plain may contain soil washed onto it from water that cut the canyon eons ago. Another, Cydonia, lies on a plain where water may be trapped in surface ice.

The first Mars Lander has been programed to put down at Chryse, at the mouth of a canyon 3,000 miles long and 20,000 feet deep. The second Lander is aimed for Cydonia, a plain on the edge of a hazy cloud cover that extends along the rim of the polar cap. If the Orbiter indicates that either or both of these locations is hazardous, one of two backup sites can be used: Tritonis Lacus, a flat region approximately 1,000 miles to the east of Chryse, and a low volcanic plain, called Alba, that shows signs of erosion.

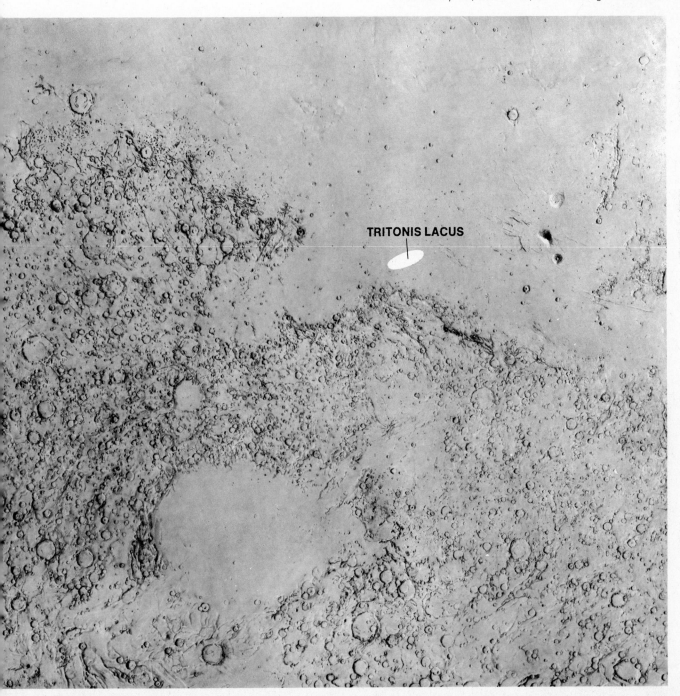

TRITONIS LACUS

Analyzing Mars on the Spot

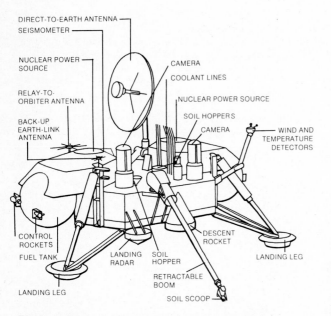

DIRECT-TO-EARTH ANTENNA
SEISMOMETER
NUCLEAR POWER SOURCE
RELAY-TO-ORBITER ANTENNA
BACK-UP EARTH-LINK ANTENNA
CAMERA
COOLANT LINES
NUCLEAR POWER SOURCE
SOIL HOPPERS
CAMERA
WIND AND TEMPERATURE DETECTORS
CONTROL ROCKETS
FUEL TANK
LANDING RADAR
SOIL HOPPER
DESCENT ROCKET
LANDING LEG
LANDING LEG
RETRACTABLE BOOM
SOIL SCOOP

The Mars Lander bristles with equipment, including a seismometer and a scoop to pick up samples for analysis of soil and a search for life. Two compact nuclear-fueled generators will provide electric power for 90 days of tests.

After settling on Mars, the Lander, the size of a small car, begins a series of tests. Twin cameras scan for signs of life, a sensor monitors winds and temperatures, and a seismometer records ground tremors. But scientists' major interest is soil, which will be analyzed for Martian life by test cells inside the Lander *(pages 92-93)*.

Three other tests will analyze Mars' surface. In one, soil is vaporized and passed through a gas chromatograph, which separates gases. These then go to a mass spectrometer, which identifies them by atomic weight and can thus detect organic substances associated with life on Earth (whether or not life is actually present). In a second test, soil is bombarded with X-rays, causing it to glow. Since the color of the glow varies according to the elements present, the soil's composition can be analyzed. In the third experiment, magnets on the scoop attract any iron-like compounds, which are then photographed by the Lander's cameras; the presence of substances such as these would indicate magnetic metals similar to those on Earth.

Hulking like a science fiction robot against the Colorado sky, a Lander mockup gets ready to dig its soil scoop into the ground. Real Landers were never allowed to touch Earth soil, for fear they might pick up microorganisms that would contaminate Martian soil samples. Before their launch, the craft were sealed in airtight capsules, then sterilized at 230°F. to kill any bacteria that might have been transferred to them by human handlers before they are secured to the tops of the Titan III/Centaur launch vehicles.

◄ Clamshell-like jaws of the soil scoop (left) dig into the soil. Attaching the jaws to the arm of the scoop is a "wrist" that rotates 360°; when the arm retracts with a sample, the scoop can turn and deposit its cargo in one of the three hoppers that feed the material to the testing devices inside.

The Viking Orbiter, shown here as a mockup, serves ► as the main link between Lander and Earth, although the Lander can communicate directly. The dish antenna (top) relays data from the Lander to Earth. The pinwheel antenna at upper left receives commands from Earth.

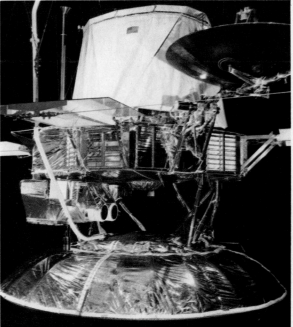

Testing for Martians in a Thimble

The Mariner-9 photographs were a letdown to those who had hoped to find bug-eyed Martians clomping around some primordial jungle. The pictures plainly revealed an austere environment, drier than the driest desert and sometimes swirling with dust storms. If life exists there, it is probably in the form of hardy microorganisms. If the microorganisms are plantlike, they would presumably use sunlight, as Earth plants do, to convert atmospheric gases into food. The Martian's life might also be animal-like, like Earth bacteria, living directly on chemical nutrients in the soil. Either life form would release waste gases that could be detected by special instruments.

Scientists spent five years perfecting a device capable of recognizing those life-revealing wastes. It weighs only 30 pounds and contains seven test cells, each the size of a thimble. They rotate on a Lazy Susan beneath a soil hopper, which portions out about one quarter of a teaspoon at a time for experiments *(right)* that may, at last, bring news of extraterrestrial life.

No larger than a breadbox, the Lander lab contains not only three fully automated biology laboratories but also a minicomputer to code data for transmittal to Earth.

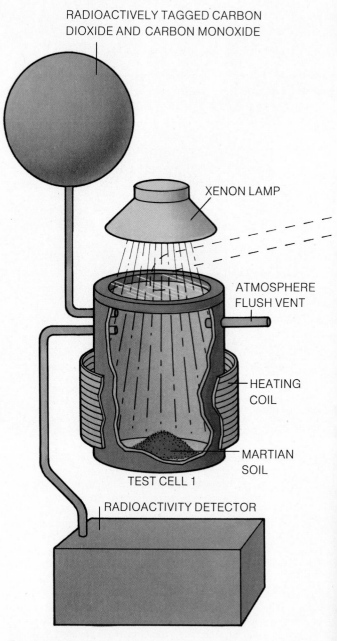

RADIOACTIVELY TAGGED CARBON DIOXIDE AND CARBON MONOXIDE

XENON LAMP

ATMOSPHERE FLUSH VENT

HEATING COIL

MARTIAN SOIL

TEST CELL 1

RADIOACTIVITY DETECTOR

Experiments begin when the soil scoop (top, center) deposits Martian soil in the hopper, which distributes it to three test cells. In the first experiment, soil is incubated under light from a xenon lamp to see if it contains living microorganisms; if it does, the light will cause the organisms to absorb molecules from the carbon-laden Martian atmosphere. Radioactive carbon is added to the soil as a tracer; after five days, the atmosphere is pumped out through a vent and the soil is heated. If vapors containing radioactive carbon are detected, they will indicate the existence of some form of Martian life.

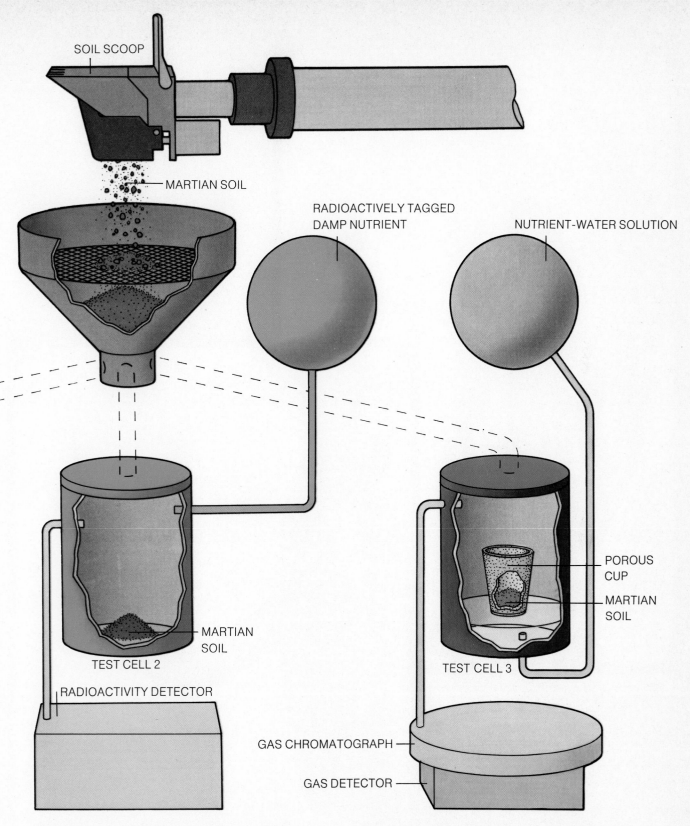

SOIL SCOOP

MARTIAN SOIL

RADIOACTIVELY TAGGED
DAMP NUTRIENT

NUTRIENT-WATER SOLUTION

POROUS
CUP

MARTIAN
SOIL

MARTIAN
SOIL

TEST CELL 2

TEST CELL 3

RADIOACTIVITY DETECTOR

GAS CHROMATOGRAPH

GAS DETECTOR

The second Lander lab experiment sniffs for wastes from animal-like Martians that might be able to exist on minute amounts of organic material and very little water. A soil sample picked up by the scoop is dropped into the test cell and fed radioactively tagged damp nutrients. Then the soil is allowed to incubate for 15 days. If microorganisms consume the nutrients, they are expected to emit waste gases such as carbon dioxide, carbon monoxide, methane. Since these organic gases will have picked up radioactivity from the tagged nutrients, their presence can be spotted by the radioactivity detector, revealing the existence of life.

The third experiment will search for wastes offering clues to any Martian life that requires a rich diet and much water. The soil in the test cell is soaked by nutrient solutions that percolate up through the bottom of a porous cup. The space above the soil sample is tested regularly by a gas chromatograph, a device that separates gases and sends them to a detector, which then identifies and measures the volumes of the gases. If the detector indicates significant amounts of carbon dioxide, methane, hydrogen, nitrogen or oxygen—all waste products of life processes—scientists will assume the gases were exhaled by microorganisms.

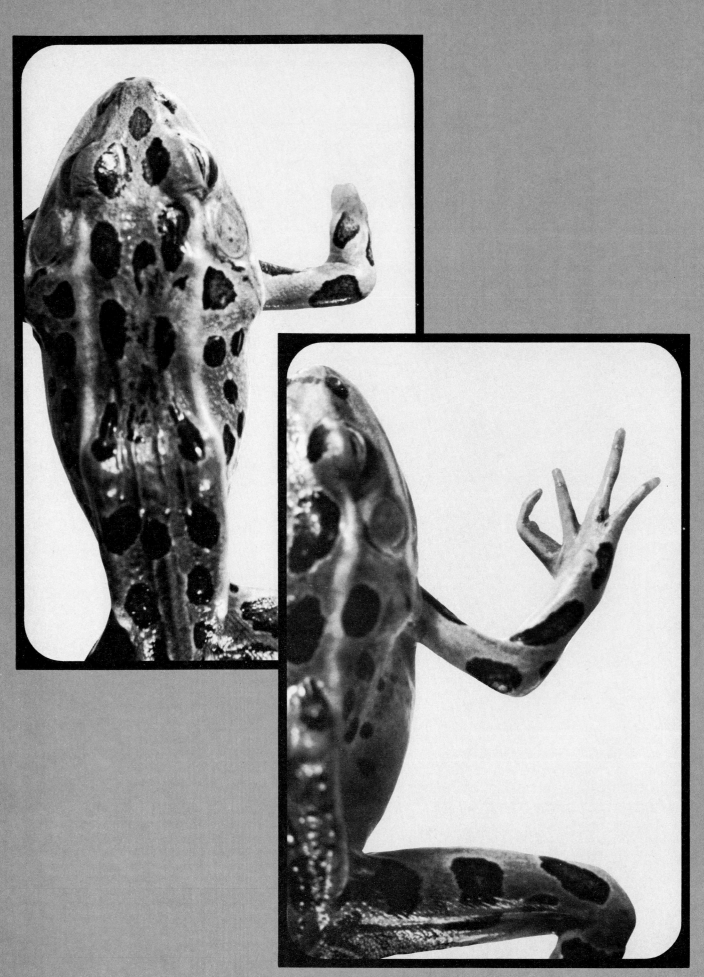

How to Grow a New Leg

AIDS TO HEALING MAY SOMEDAY RESTORE LOST BODY PARTS

by Graham Chedd

Man can outthink the salamander. But in evolving a brain, he lost something the salamander, given the choice, might be unwilling to give up: the ability to regrow a missing limb or a damaged heart. Cut a leg off a salamander, and the stump soon sprouts a new one—bone, skin, nerves, joints and all—in two months. A man can grow a new fingernail, but not a finger; his shattered bones can knit and his torn skin replaces itself, but a lost arm or leg is lost forever.

Now new experiments suggest that humans might one day gain the salamander's ability to regenerate. In 1975 a New York orthopedic surgeon, Dr. Andrew Bassett of Columbia University's College of Physicians and Surgeons, reported that five children, born with defects that kept the bones of their lower legs in a rubbery state, were made normal by regenerating the defective bones with tiny electric currents. In addition nearly 100 other people who had faced amputation because of diseased bones have also been healed by such "bioelectronic" means.

Some researchers think bioelectronics may even heal heart muscles scarred in a heart attack, or prompt the regeneration of whole limbs. And the electrical approach to regeneration is not the only one. Similar effects with a chemical stimulus are foreseen by scientists such as Marcus Singer of Case Western Reserve University, Cleveland. Says Dr. Robert Becker of the Veterans Administration Hospital, Syracuse, New York, a pioneer in the field, "We are on the threshold of a new era in medicine."

Which of the two approaches—the electrical or the chemical—will prove the more fruitful is a

Electric currents applied to the stump of a frog's amputated foreleg (top) stimulated the growth of a new "hand"—even though an adult frog, unlike more primitive creatures, cannot ordinarily regenerate lost limbs. Similar treatment of human patients has speeded healing of bone injuries.

hotly debated issue, for the ability to regenerate is as yet little understood. The power to repair lost or damaged tissue is a basic ability of all living things. Indeed, it is essential; without the capacity to mend bones or heal wounds no species could survive long in the rough-and-tumble of natural selection. The more primitive the animal, the better it is at putting itself back together. Very lowly animals like sponges can be squeezed through a sieve and broken down into their individual cells; the cells can then reassociate into an intact creature. A hydra, slightly higher up the evolutionary scale, can survive the guillotine: cut off its head, and it simply grows back.

More complex creatures possess a more limited capacity for regeneration. Salamanders and newts can grow new tails and legs, and even up to 50 per cent of their hearts. Tadpoles regrow limbs too, but they lose the ability as they mature into frogs. Mammals, man included, are capable of regenerating only bone, and that to no more than a limited extent.

Regeneration seems to be a special kind of healing ability, a different version of the process by which animals routinely replace nails, skin, hair, feathers and scales. Part of the process is somewhat similar to the way in which the regenerated cells grew originally in the fetus before birth. In the first days of an animal's prenatal life, the cells are all alike. As the fetus grows, however, the cells begin to specialize into the many different types demanded by the newborn: skin, bone, blood, nerves and all the rest. This "differentiation" seems to go temporarily into reverse in regeneration. At the site of a fracture in a human bone, for instance, cells adjacent to the break seem to sense the damage and revert to an embryonic state. They act as they did in the fetus, first being unspecialized, then forming specific types needed. As they recapitulate the sequence of events that created them in the first place, they regenerate the lost bone.

The process can be observed most clearly when a salamander's limb is amputated. The tip of the stump, in about 10 days, forms a tiny bud of rapidly dividing, undifferentiated cells called a blastema. Soon the growth begins to become organized. Specialized cells that will form bone,

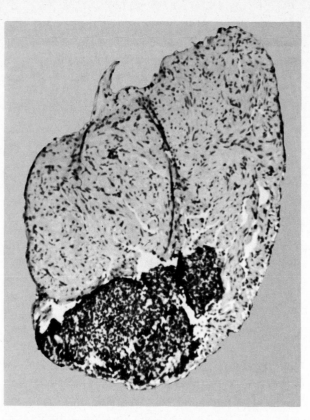

Two hours after a third of a salamander heart was cut away, primitive new cells—the dark masses on this microscopic section—appeared. These cells were the first evidence that an animal like the salamander, which can regenerate limbs, also can regrow its heart tissue.

muscle and tendon start to develop. The limb grows a hint of an elbow and a hand, and minute nubs appear that grow into fingers. After another month the limb is as good as new.

The why and how of regeneration have puzzled scientists for more than 200 years. Among the first to be impressed by the remarkable regenerative ability of amphibians was an 18th Century Italian biologist-priest, Lazzaro Spallanzani. In 1768 he wondered why, if amphibious creatures could regenerate limbs, "other land animals, such as are accounted perfect, and are better known to us, are not endowed with the same power? Is it to be hoped that they may acquire them by some useful dispositions? And should the flattering expectation of obtaining this advantage for ourselves be entirely chimerical?"

The first clue to the possibility of acquiring such a "disposition" came a half century later, when an Englishman, Tweedy John Todd, showed that nerves are essential to the salamanders' capacity for regeneration. He severed the nerve leading to the amputated stump of a salamander and found that the stump then simply shriveled away. After a few days, however, the nerve grew back into the stump and thereupon started to regenerate the amputated limb.

The observation that nerves play some crucial role in regeneration has been confirmed repeatedly in the 150 years since Todd's first experiments. One dramatic confirmation came in the early 1950s, when C. W. Bodemer of the University of Washington produced an extra forelimb, complete with toes, from the upper part of a salamander's leg simply by shifting a nerve from its normal position in the limb to a different site on the same limb.

At about this time another significant discovery was made by Marcus Singer, then working at Cornell. A frog was known to lose its powers of regeneration as it matured from the tadpole stage. This loss, Singer reasoned, might be connected to nerve changes. As the tadpole develops, the density of nerve tissue in its limbs gradually diminishes in proportion to the other tissues. He wondered if there existed a minimum number of nerve fibers in a limb, below which their influence was insufficient to promote regeneration. Singer tested the idea by giving extra nerves to a frog that had long outgrown its tadpole capacity for regeneration. He first amputated a forelimb of the adult frog, then drew the long sciatic nerve from a hind limb and repositioned it in the forelimb stump. The increase in nerve supply restored to the stump the lost capacity to regenerate its forelimb.

It is now generally accepted that nerves supply some ingredient that initiates regeneration. Why the nerves perform this function in primitive animals but not in advanced ones has been suggested by both Robert Becker and Marcus Singer. They point out that as organisms have evolved and become more complex, more and more of their nervous tissue has been concentrated in the brain. This tendency has been accompanied by a reduction in the amount of tissue in the peripheral nervous system of the body. As a result, the volume of nerves in, say, a human

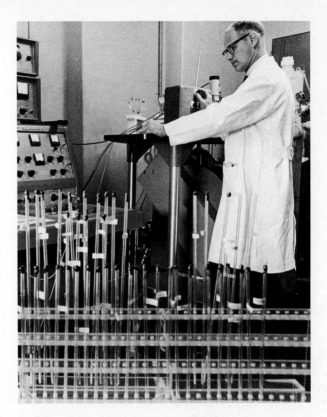

Dr. Robert Becker, who argues that electric currents, not chemicals, cause regeneration, tests human bone (in the tubes, foreground) for currents they produce under stress. Such natural currents in bone, Becker says, may explain why it regenerates and most other human tissue does not.

arm, is below the threshold at which it can initiate regeneration.

But what signal do nerves send out to stimulate regeneration? In attempting to answer this question, Singer and Becker have taken different theoretical and experimental paths. Singer believes the signal to be chemical, and Becker is convinced that it is electrical. Since nerves use both chemical and electrical signals in their role as communication pathways, either mechanism is plausible. Both scientists present sound evidence to support their views, and Becker can point to practical results that have been achieved with electrical treatments.

Becker began his interest in bioelectricity by investigating an electrical phenomenon known as the current of injury. When tissue is damaged a small current appears near the injury, flowing between the damaged and the healthy tissue. Most scientists interpreted the current

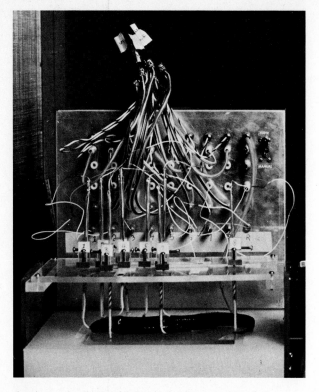

A salamander (bottom) is hooked up to a machine that records changes in body electricity when tissue is injured. After a limb of the salamander was amputated, electrical changes were recorded all over the animal's nervous system, but especially in the brain—which processed the S O S from the site of the injury and then sent back a message that somehow stimulated the cells to regenerate.

of conducting ordinary nerve signals back and forth between the brain and sensory organs —an information-transmitting operation carried out by means of complex electrochemical reactions. In the other, more primitive, basic role, the nerves send very small currents in the same way that a wire does. It is this latter system, Becker believes, that is involved in controlling all healing processes, including regeneration.

Becker suggests that these tiny healing currents, millions of times weaker than those required for a flashlight, are carried by the membrane that sheathes all nerve fibers; and that the passage of such very small currents was the original function of the nervous system when it developed in primitive organisms. Only later did the stronger, more efficient electrochemical means of signal transmission evolve. However, the original system has been retained, he postulates, to do what it has always done: control the healing process.

Becker thinks that the current of injury developed at a wound site warns the body, via this system, that a wound has occurred. A still unidentified control site interprets the warning and sends back to the injury site a current that directs the cells to cope with the injury. In animals like salamanders, he believes, this current is large enough to trigger the full process of regeneration. In man, where the peripheral nervous system is scantier, and the electrical regeneration signal therefore weaker, only modest healing takes place.

The exception is bone. After breaking, bone is capable of regenerating to fill in the fracture zone. Yet bone is only scantily supplied with nerves. This seeming paradox actually provides strong support for Becker's ideas about electricity, for bone is able to generate its own electrical effects under stress.

Bone has a remarkable capacity for adapting itself to stress by laying down extra material on the side under compression, and dissolving material from the side being stretched. Scientists showed some 20 years ago that the compressed side of the bone becomes electrically negative while the side under tension becomes positive.

Assuming that these electrical phenomena

of injury as arising from electrochemical action in the ruptured membranes of damaged cells, and did not consider its significance in regeneration. But when Becker and his colleagues studied the current of injury in frogs and salamanders that had had their forelimbs amputated, an interesting difference between the two species emerged. In the frog, which does not regenerate, the electrical effect disappeared as the stump healed over, but in the salamander it lingered, slowly declining as regeneration proceeded until it finally disappeared when the limb was complete.

These experiments led Becker to formulate the idea that the current of injury is intimately associated with the regenerative process. His subsequent studies have allowed him to refine this hypothesis. He now views the nervous system as having two roles. One is its familiar job

caused the growth and dissolution of bone at sites of stress, Becker, working with Andrew Bassett, reasoned that an applied current should also have the same effect. In 1964 they inserted two small electrodes into the bone of a dog's hind leg and connected a battery to the electrodes. With a current of about five millionths of that consumed in a 100-watt bulb, new bone growth was indeed stimulated around the negative electrode.

The experiment created a great deal of interest. The next half-dozen years saw several research groups experimenting with the effect of small electric currents on mending bone—the most promising part of the body to try since it regenerates naturally in all animals. A typical test showed that a current comparable to the one employed by Becker and Bassett doubled the normal healing rate of bones in rabbits.

ELECTRICITY TO HEAL BROKEN BONES

The original attempts to use electricity to mend broken bones in humans concentrated on two kinds of cases that were difficult to treat normally. In the first, the broken bone of the patient had not properly knitted, either because of faulty treatment or because of some unrelated illness (diabetics, for example, have poor circulation, which cuts down on the supply of materials to the healing area). The second condition was a rare bone disorder known as pseudarthrosis, in which part of the tissue that should normally develop as bone develops instead as wobbly, cartilage-like tissue.

One of the first successes with electrical healing of bone came in the fall of 1970, when Dr. Leroy Lavine of the State University of New York treated a 14-year-old suffering from pseudarthrosis of the tibia, the main bone of the lower leg. Several attempts had been made to mend the bone using other treatments, such as bone grafts, but after the boy had fractured his repaired leg in an accident it seemed that amputation was the only remaining recourse. Because the leg could be saved no other way, Lavine and his colleagues decided to try electricity.

The surgical team implanted two platinum electrodes in the bone on either side of the frac-

ture site and used two flashlight batteries to pass a current between them. Four months later the fracture had healed, and before long the boy was walking normally.

Another early success was achieved by a group under Dr. Carl Brighton at the University of Philadelphia School of Medicine. A 51-year-old woman had broken her ankle falling down stairs. The fracture had failed to mend properly, causing the patient pain for over a year. The Philadelphia team implanted a stainless-steel electrode within a hole drilled into the fracture site and placed a second electrode, an aluminum grid, on the surface of the skin. A current was kept flowing between the electrodes for nine weeks; by then the fracture had healed.

Since these two early experiments, nearly 100 patients have been treated in the United States and well over 1,000 elsewhere have benefited from electrical bone healing. In Australia, for example, doctors are exploring the possibility of using the treatment to strengthen the spines of patients with back problems.

Bassett has recently introduced a refinement of the technique. Concerned over the necessity for surgery at the fracture site, he began searching for a way to create an electric current at the fracture without inserting electrodes. After several years of laboratory experiments—first on living cells in test tubes, then on animals—he turned to electromagnetism and applied the principle of the transformer. Coils outside a limb were fed a pulsing current, which created a pulsing electromagnetic field. A pulsing field induces a current to flow in any conductor nearby—and since bone cells are conductors of a sort, a current was induced inside the bone between the electrodes. When such currents were induced in the broken bones of dogs, they cut the healing time of fractures by as much as 50 per cent.

Although there is some question about the possibility of harm from strong electromagnetic fields (page 174), this method was employed by Bassett to treat five children with pseudarthrosis. He simply cut two small windows in the plaster cast encasing the leg of each child and placed in each window a rectangular coil of insulated wire. The coils were plugged into an electric power source for 16 hours a day, leaving plenty of time for work and play. The results were excellent: One young girl has remained free of the disease for almost two years, and the other children for from seven to 10 months. None exhibited ill effects from the electromagnetic field. Bassett is now attempting to develop completely portable systems that can be built into plaster casts, and he plans to try the technique in the treatment of fresh fractures and joint and ligament injuries —they constitute the third largest group of hospital cases in the United States, about 10 million every year.

Robert Becker aims higher yet. He proposes to do more than improve the healing of bone, which can regenerate itself naturally anyway. He sees Bassett's treatment as only a step—albeit an important one—toward restoring to humans the ability to regenerate other parts of the body. Recent animal experiments support this hope.

In 1967 Stephen Smith, a professor of anatomy at the University of Kentucky in Lexington, induced the partial regeneration of a frog's amputated forelimb with a modified version of the electrical healing technique: He implanted within this stump a small strip made up of two dissimilar metals. The strip served as a self-activating battery—a current flows between dissimilar metals in a salt solution such as body fluids. A similar technique was used by Becker in 1972 to induce some regeneration of the amputated limbs of laboratory rats. And in 1973 Smith implanted battery-powered electrodes inside the foreleg stumps of amputee grass frogs. Smith used 21 frogs in all. In every one he obtained some regeneration, but in five animals dramatic regeneration occurred: One of the animals developed a complete forelimb.

In experiments with rabbits, Becker himself has used small electric currents to regenerate completely the cartilage in rabbit joints. He is, he says, 99 per cent certain that the same result could be achieved with humans. Cartilage must be regenerated, of course, if limbs are to be regrown. And, more immediately, restoration of cartilage would be a boon in the treatment of arthritis, which is caused when damaged cartilage turns into stiff and often painful scar tissue.

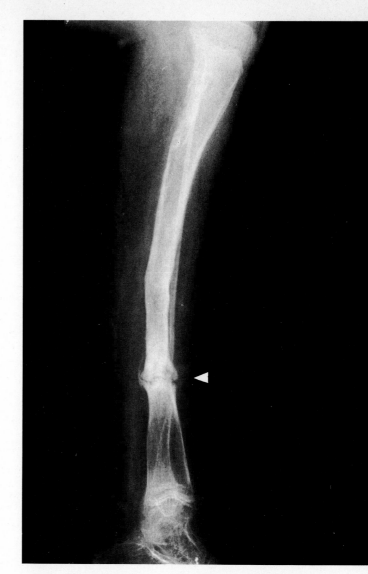

An X-ray shows the broken shinbone (arrow) of a 10-year-old girl with pseudarthritic—nonhealing—bone tissue that has been mended (right) with a new electric treatment.

Further off, Becker sees the possibility of regeneration in other organs that at present heal by scarring. One dramatic possibility lies in the treatment of heart-attack victims. A heart attack results in the death of a portion of the heart muscle. The damage heals by scarring, holding the heart together but permanently impairing its effectiveness as a pump. Becker speculates that implanted electrical devices might one day make it possible to regenerate the dead tissue of the heart, obviating the need for such radical treatments as heart transplants or artificial hearts.

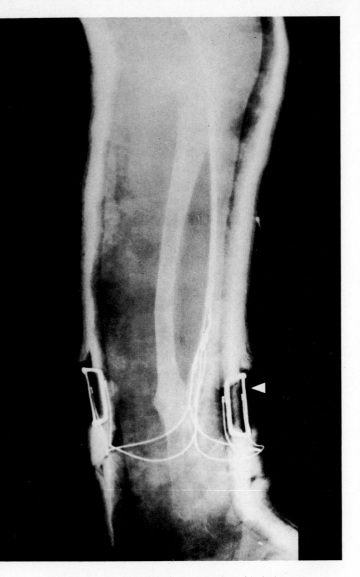

A pair of coils of insulated wire are placed in holes cut in the girl's cast on either side of the fracture (at bottom) and a small current is sent pulsing across the shinbone.

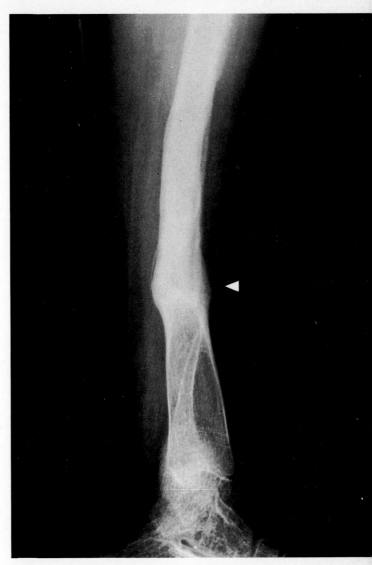

After four months of electrical stimulation, the previously untreatable break has knit perfectly, dispelling the threat of amputation and allowing the child to resume a normal life.

Of course the ultimate goal of those involved in the study of regeneration is the complete restoration of a complex, multitissue structure such as an arm or a leg. Becker, Smith and Bassett have come a considerable way toward such a fantastic achievement. Their experiments with electrical stimulation have shown that some body parts can indeed be reconstituted in ways never before thought possible. While such dramatic successes in practical healing cannot yet be claimed by those seeking a chemical rather than an electrical restorative, their work is now on a seemingly solid theoretical basis, and the ultimate goal of complete restoration appears to be within their grasp, too.

The leader in the search for a chemical signal for regeneration, Marcus Singer, has derived his own explanation for the regrowth of tissue from his experiments in transplanting nerves. The process, he believes, involves the production by nerves of a powerful growth-stimulating chemical, which he calls the trophic factor. Singer points out that a possible source for this factor already exists: the cellular matter, or cytoplasm, that sustains nerve fibers. Cytoplasm is supplied in a continuous flow from the central nervous system. When the stream of cytoplasm reaches the end of a nerve fiber, some of it spills over into the surrounding tissue. In Singer's words, "We can think of the nerve fibers as bleeding at their ends." If there are enough nerve endings, sufficient quantities of the trophic factor will spill out of the ends to initiate regeneration. If the factor could be identified and isolated, then it could perhaps be injected into damaged human tissue to stimulate regeneration.

Singer has spent many years developing a delicate technique for finding the trophic factor. First he prepares a variety of chemical extracts from the ground-up nervous tissue of newts and frogs. Then he amputates a newt's forelimbs. When the stumps have healed over and produced the bud that indicates regeneration has started, he removes the nerve supply from one stump, halting regeneration. The other stump acts as a control. Using a very fine microsyringe, Singer then infuses into the nerveless stump a solution of the extract under test. If the extract starts the regenerative process operating again—even microscopically—then it presumably contains the trophic factor normally supplied by the nerve.

Determining whether the test extract has any effect at all is a major problem—whatever regeneration occurs is too slight to be visible. Singer therefore has to monitor the process by injecting radioactive molecules into the newt's belly and then measuring radioactivity changes to determine the rate at which the molecules are taken up in the stump. He compares this stump with the stump that still has its nerves intact to see if both grow at the same rate; if so he can assume he is on the way to identifying the trophic factor.

Despite the intricacy of the operation, it has produced some intriguing results. Singer's crude extract is already remarkably potent, able to stimulate some regeneration even when diluted many-fold, and he believes he is now very close to obtaining a reasonably pure preparation of the factor. He has found that an extract taken from the frog is just as effective in stimulating regeneration in the newt limb bud as is a newt extract, implying that the factor is a fundamental one,

Marcus Singer, who holds that the regrowth of body parts is caused by a chemical flowing from damaged nerve ends, injects one amputated forelimb of a newt (closeup, above) with a chemical derived from a newt's nerves, brain or liver. Later tests showed that the chemical had stimulated a minute amount of regeneration, although the newt's normal regenerating mechanism had been neutralized.

common to many different kinds of species. (One odd result of the experiments is the discovery that newts seem to be much better at regenerating their limbs in the spring and summer than they are in the fall and winter.)

Even though it may seem that Singer's nerve chemical has no connection to Becker's nerve currents, the history of discovery in biology has shown repeatedly that the dividing line between chemistry and electricity is blurred: phenomena thought chemical have turned out to be partly electrical, and vice versa. Regeneration, too, might involve both electrical and chemical signals, perhaps interacting in some manner. But whatever the nature of the "useful dispositions" of regeneration, there is little doubt that when they are finally pinned down they will cause a revolution in medicine.

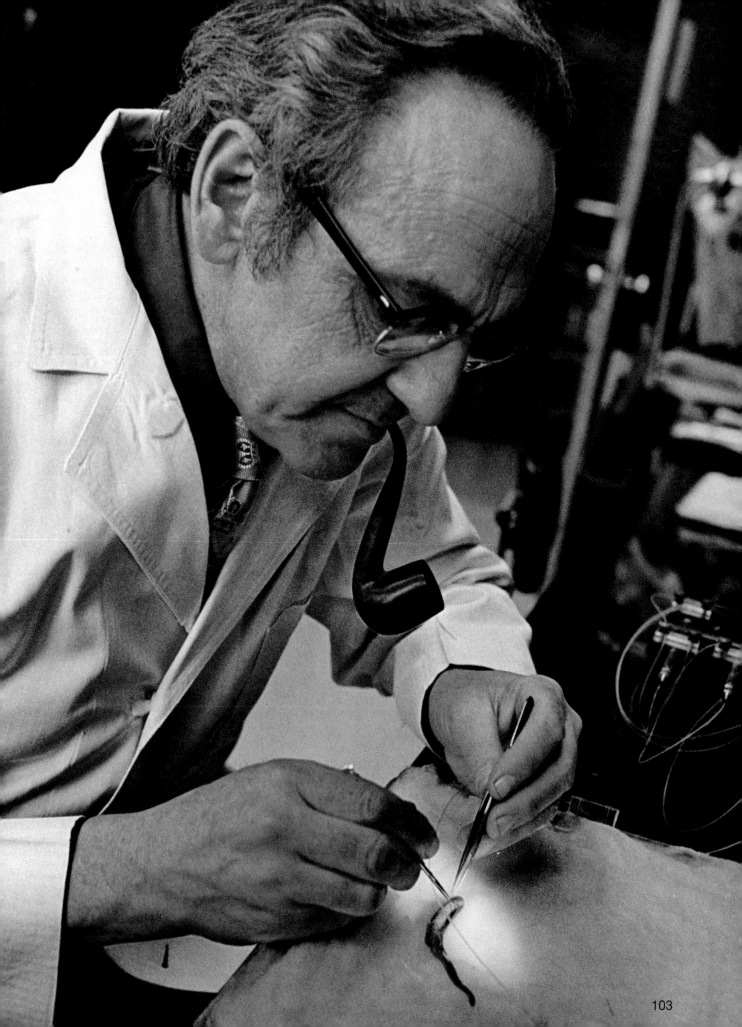

Close Look at Southern Skies

To astronomers, one of the most important parts of the sky is the region between the earth and the center of our galaxy—the vast system of stars, called the Milky Way, that includes the sun. In this space is the richest mixture of celestial objects found anywhere in the heavens —clouds of cosmic gas called nebulae, exploded star remnants and great stellar agglomerations. But this part of the sky can be seen best from the Southern Hemisphere, which until now has lacked the powerful telescopes available in the north: Its biggest instrument had been less than half the size of the giant 200-inch reflector at Palomar in California. That situation has suddenly changed dramatically.

In both Chile and Australia, two kinds of new telescopes began to turn up important fresh data in 1975. Each country now has a reflecting telescope second in size only to the Palomar instrument. Each also has a big new wide-angle telescope, used for broad-area surveys of the sky. The telescopes are set up close to the 29th parallel, the latitude at which the galactic center passes exactly overhead at night for six months of the year, giving astronomers their first good view of the strange territory in the southern sky.

The new southern connection proved its worth almost immediately. In 1975, one of the test photographs taken with the 158-inch telescope at Cerro Tololo, Chile, turned out to be a startling astronomical first: It revealed thin wisps of luminous gas twisting away from a galaxy of stars in the constellation Centaurus to nearby spots that emit radio waves. Astronomers had assumed a link between some galaxies and nearby radio sources, but a direct physical link had never been seen until the Chile photographs revealed one, in the form of faint gas, sending matter from a visible star to a radio offspring.

A technician examines the 158-inch Cerro Tololo mirror in light from a laser at Kitt Peak National Observatory, Tucson, Arizona, where the mirror was ground. Shadows on the mirror detect irregularities as slight as one millionth of an inch, indicating portions that need further polishing.

A Powerful Telescope Built for Chile

On June 25, 1969, 35 tons of blazing-hot liquid glass was poured into a cylindrical mold, 158 inches in interior diameter and 30 inches high, at the Owens-Illinois plant in Toledo. The telescope mirror for Cerro Tololo, Chile, was born. The pouring took 13.5 minutes, but another five years elapsed before the mirror was ground *(top, right)* and set up atop Cerro Tololo Mountain.

The mirror owes much of its effectiveness to a new substance, Cer-Vit. Unlike ordinary glass, which has molecules mixed at all angles, Cer-Vit has molecules lined up in a regular crystalline structure that helps it hold shape as temperature changes. Such stability is an obvious advantage in a telescope mirror, since sharp focus depends on shape—an advantage proved by Cerro Tololo's perception of faint links between visible and radio stars in the constellation Centaurus.

Assaying the progress of the 158-inch mirror's grinding, a square screen pierced by 440 holes is lowered to one inch above the mirror. Light from a tungsten lamp shines through the holes and bounces off the mirror, then bounces back through holes in the screen and is photographed by a camera behind the screen. The photographic dot pattern shows what irregularities must be ground off.

◄ *The Cerro Tololo telescope aims through the opening of its 13-story-high domed building. The 15-ton mirror, cradled in its 375-ton mounting, is swung into position, along with the dome opening, by automatic machinery.*

A view of the luminous gas cloud around the star Eta Carinae is provided by a test photograph taken with the new telescope. Astronomers watch this nebula because stars may be born in the small dark patches of dust scattered amid the glowing gas.

An Instrument on Watch Down Under

Australian astronomers have long been world leaders in radio astronomy, the study of radio waves emitted from sky objects. But until now they have lacked the optical instruments that would help them match their radio observations with light-wave data. Today they have what they need: The 154-inch telescope at Siding Spring, New South Wales, is a box seat for sky watching.

The instrument will study sky objects that have already been observed with Australia's radio telescopes, but have rarely (or never) been recorded in high-power photographs: radio stars, as well as quasars, the mysterious radio-wave sources that seem to be situated at the very edge of the universe. But it also records breathtaking views of visible galaxies, star clusters and gas clouds *(below and opposite)*.

The 154-inch Siding Spring telescope, just completing its final tests, aims upward to record unusual events in the little-studied galaxies of the Southern Hemisphere.

This spiral galaxy in the constellation Dorado underwent an unprecedented change over six years, changing from a turbulent mass of stars into a suddenly quiet one.

The globular cluster 47 Tucanae contains at least 10 million stars. This photograph from Siding Spring records two to three times more of them than have ever been seen before.

New stars appear to be forming at a rapid pace in the Tarantula Nebula, a luminous mass of gas around the star 30 Doradus embedded in the large Magellanic Cloud.

A Joint Project to Map Little-Known Stars

The southern hemisphere's so-called Schmidt telescopes—wide-angle instruments combining a lens and a mirror, which were designed by Bernard Schmidt in 1931—are as essential to the study of the southern sky as the huge reflectors. The 48-inch Schmidt at Siding Spring, Australia, with the 39-inch at La Silla, Chile, will produce a photographic atlas of southern stars, including many areas poorly charted until now.

Such an atlas is necessary because the big reflectors see only one tiny section of the sky at a time. To interpret such observations, astronomers need to know what lies nearby; in the new atlas photographs, they will know at a glance.

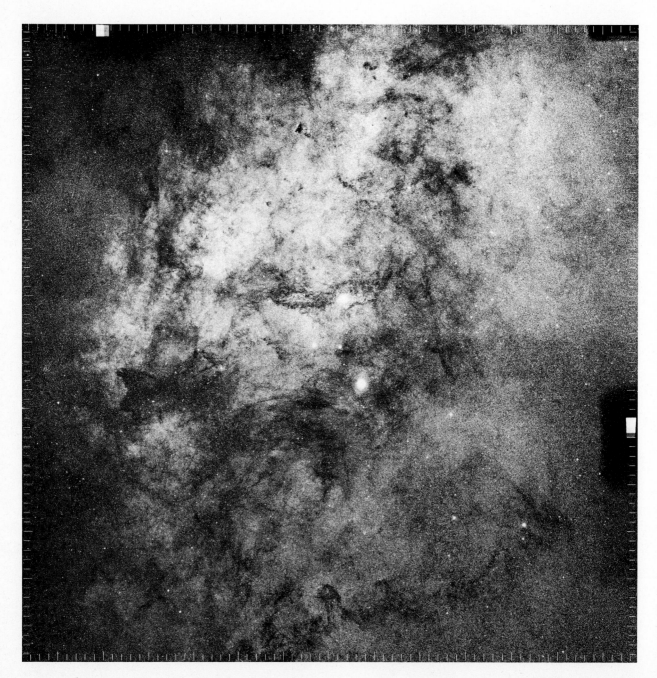

Stars nearly fill a photograph of a part of Sagittarius adjacent to the galactic center. The Siding Spring Schmidt telescope, one of the world's largest, recorded about three times as many stars as most instruments can pick up.

Inside the sleek shell of the Siding Spring Schmidt are a 48- ▶ *inch lens at the front end and, at the lower end, a mirror made of temperature-resistant crystalline glass. The small telescopes attached to the side are used for aiming.*

Probing the Invisible Universe

There is a simple reason behind the boom in telescopes in South America and Australia *(pages 106-113):* Discoveries of recent decades have thrown into turmoil the previously well-ordered world of astronomy. And many of the questions raised by those discoveries can best be answered with the help of observations from the Southern Hemisphere.

Until the early 1960s, astronomers had been studying a universe they thought they understood. The bulk of their information came from optical telescopes, those that, like the ones on the preceding pages, used lenses and mirrors to make photographs of the heavens' visible objects.

The flourishing in the 1950s of radio astronomy, based not on optical photographic records, but on the use of radio receivers and wire antennas to observe radio signals from the sky, did little more than extend knowledge along familiar lines. Equipment was too crude to do more, and the earth's atmosphere blocks a large proportion of the radio waves from space. This same atmospheric obstacle limited observations of infrared and ultraviolet rays, and it practically prevented detection of gamma rays and X-rays, which hardly penetrate the air at all.

Then, in the early 1960s, refined techniques and improved equipment became available. More important, the blinders imposed by the earth's atmosphere could be removed: balloons and spacecraft were now capable of lifting sizable instruments above the ground. With the information gathered by these so-phisticated techniques, the astronomers' complacent world shattered.

The new observations made clear that violence pervades the invisible universe. Exploding galaxies were seen to be throwing off energy in the form of ultraviolet and X-ray radiation in staggering amounts, far more than predicted by observations of visible light. The hidden nucleus of the earth's own Milky Way galaxy was revealed as a powerful emitter of radio waves. Mysterious "X-ray stars," invisible to earthbound telescopes, turned up, and two new types of sky objects were discovered, unlike anything ever known before: quasars, short for quasi-stellar objects, and pulsars, so called because their radiation pulses regularly, as fast as 30 times per second.

It is small wonder that astronomers' appetites were whetted by such tantalizing glimpses of the unseen universe. More instruments were needed to provide opportunities for observation; new techniques had to be developed to record as much as possible of the many signals from the sky and to locate radio sources with the accuracy that optical telescopes attain on visible stars.

Perhaps most pressing was the need to correlate the flood of new data on radio waves, X-rays, infrared and ultraviolet with records of the visible sky. This requirement placed heavy demands on optical telescopes. Although new instruments were built in various locations, the need was greatest in the Southern Hemisphere, where there had been no large

Gamma rays, radio waves and other radiation from space are forms of energy making up the electromagnetic spectrum *(below). Some forms are seen as light, infrared is* felt as heat, but all differ only in their wavelengths—the shorter ones (left) have more energy. Boundaries between types overlap because the waves' behavior overlaps.

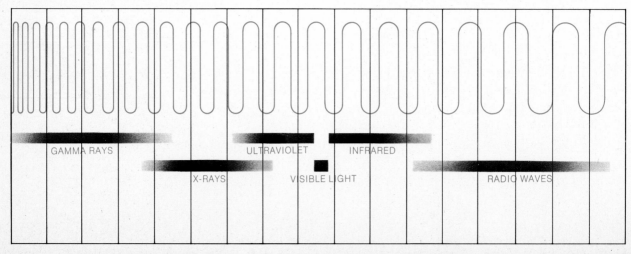

GAMMA RAYS

ULTRAVIOLET

INFRARED

X-RAYS

VISIBLE LIGHT

RADIO WAVES

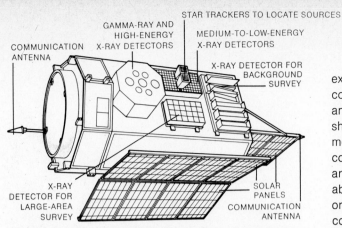

STAR TRACKERS TO LOCATE SOURCES

GAMMA-RAY AND HIGH-ENERGY X-RAY DETECTORS

MEDIUM-TO-LOW-ENERGY X-RAY DETECTORS

COMMUNICATION ANTENNA

X-RAY DETECTOR FOR BACKGROUND SURVEY

X-RAY DETECTOR FOR LARGE-AREA SURVEY

SOLAR PANELS

COMMUNICATION ANTENNA

The first High Energy Astronomy Observatory will launch in 1977, carrying a battery of detectors to sort out gamma rays and high-energy X-rays from the less energetic X-rays. Earth stations will control the solar-powered satellite.

optical instruments but many fruitful observations of radio sources.

Still under construction is the largest (120-inch) telescope ever designed exclusively for infrared work, begun in 1974 near the summit of Mauna Kea, a snow-capped volcano on the big island of Hawaii. The 13,780-foot altitude of the observatory makes it the highest on earth. At that height, the earth's atmosphere offers little hindrance to infrared waves because there is only one tenth as much water vapor, which absorbs infrared energy, as there is near sea level. The National Aeronautics and Space Administration (NASA), which is building the instrument, hopes to put it in service in early 1977 for studies of temperatures and surface details of planets and their satellites, particularly Jupiter and Saturn.

The renewed emphasis on optical telescopes has not slowed the building of larger, more precise instruments for detecting other celestial signals. In the domain of radio astronomy, the National Radio Astronomy Observatory's Very Large Array, or VLA, is expected to begin shakedown tests in 1976 near Socorro, New Mexico. The VLA will use 27 dish-shaped antennas, each 82 feet in diameter, arranged in a Y-shaped pattern *(below)*. Because the dishes are movable, it will be possible to space the antennas to conform to any one of four basic schemes. When the array is stretched to its full 26-mile length, it will be able to separate details in radio sources to within one tenth of a second of arc—a resolution of detail comparable to that of the world's largest and most precise optical telescope, the 200 inch at Mount Palomar in California.

The sensitivity of the array can also be increased, at some sacrifice of resolution, in order to detect very faint sources; the antennas need only be concentrated closer to the center of the Y.

X-rays, gamma rays and cosmic rays from space will be the target of orbiting High-Energy Astronomy Observatories (HEAO), which NASA plans to launch in 1977, 1978 and 1979. The first, designated HEAO-A *(above, left),* will sweep the sky for X-ray and gamma-ray sources, map the stronger ones, and survey an overall diffuse X-ray and gamma-ray background. Following up on these observations, HEAO-B will study in detail the more important of the X-ray sources discovered, while HEAO-C will collect gamma-ray and cosmic-ray data.

The most important astronomical studies in years to come cannot even be guessed at, let alone planned. Every major improvement in astronomical devices has opened new vistas, from Galileo's discovery of Jupiter's four bright satellites with the very first telescope to the fortuitous recording of cosmic radio waves by Karl Jansky in 1932. The new projects, and others like them, are likely once again to revolutionize man's concept of his universe.

When tests start in 1976, the 27 mobile radio telescopes of the Very Large Array, now under construction near Socorro, New Mexico, will either stand in close proximity *(as in this drawing) to receive faint radio sources, or will be spaced out along the Y-shaped grid to provide a more detailed picture of the celestial objects under study.*

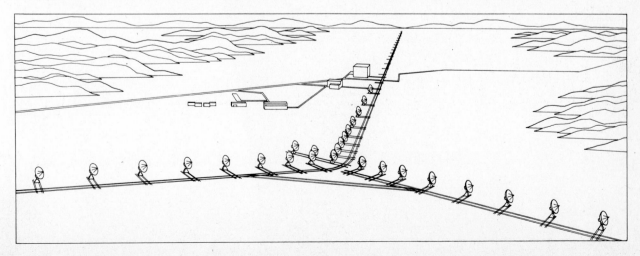

The Great Spray-Can Scare

THEIR CHEMICALS MAY BE HARMING THE STRATOSPHERE

by Ogden Tanner

At first the idea seemed bizarre, preposterous, the latest and most improbable dirty joke played by nature on man's technology. But there it was, in the newspapers and the scholarly journals, in the earnest, worried testimony of a host of scientists before committees of the United States Senate and House. As the evidence mounted, the implications became increasingly clear: Every *psst* of underarm deodorant, every *pfft* of pressurized hairspray, every *poof* of bathroom cleaner was adding to a new and disturbing atmospheric contamination. The ultimate, unwitting villain in the tragedy of the environment, it appeared, could turn out to be the innocent consumer with his finger on the push button of the aerosol bomb.

The problem had nothing to do with deodorants or hairsprays as such, or with the 300-odd other products now packaged in pressure cans, but with the colorless, tasteless, odorless gases that are used to propel them out the nozzle. These synthetic compounds of carbon, chlorine and fluorine—commonly called fluorocarbons, or Freons after the trade name given to them by their largest manufacturer, DuPont—are used because they are nontoxic, nonflammable, almost totally inert and do not react with the can's contents or nearly anything else.

Ironically, however, it was their very stability that suddenly seemed to make them a potential danger. Indestructible by normal atmospheric processes at lower altitudes, the invisible gases

What comes out of a spray can is not only deodorant, hair spray, perfume or whatever (dark particles) but also the fluorocarbon gas (surrounding white area) that propels the product from the can. The colorless, odorless and seemingly innocuous gas, made visible here by special photography, eventually floats into the stratosphere.

could gradually build up over a period of years and find their way into the upper atmosphere; there, in the stratosphere, ultraviolet radiation of the sun—energetic radiation in wavelengths shorter than those violet rays in the visible spectrum—could break them down into their chemical components, with some potentially damaging results to life on earth below.

Two fluorocarbon components, chlorine and fluorine, are extremely reactive gases. Fluorine quickly combines with other elements of the atmosphere to form stable compounds and is thus safely out of the way. Chlorine reacts, too, but in a different manner, continually joining with and breaking away from atoms of oxygen. In doing so, it transforms one particular form of oxygen, called ozone, into ordinary oxygen, steadily depleting the stratosphere's ozone supply.

DAMAGING THE EARTH'S PROTECTIVE SHIELD

Ozone is a very special substance. It forms a gauzy, invisible blanket in the stratosphere, 12 to 30 miles above the earth, shielding the planet from those ultraviolet solar rays that are most dangerous to living cells. With this protective shield damaged, scientists have envisioned a variety of long-term consequences, including a rise in the rate of human skin cancer, increased problems with sunburn and eye injuries, and incalculable effect on plant and animal life. Worse still, it appeared that similar effects might be caused by a number of other substances that could reach the stratosphere from various sources: methyl chloride from sewage-treatment and water-purification plants, carbon tetrachloride

from natural and industrial sources and nitric oxide from the exhausts of high-flying supersonic airplanes, and perhaps even from agriculture.

Just how serious the "ozone problem" might be, on what time scale, and what to do about it came under close scientific and public scrutiny in 1975. Both the United States Senate and House of Representatives, as well as states from New York to California, held hearings at which atmospheric physicists, chemists and representatives of the fluorocarbon industry were invited to testify. The quasi-official National Academy of Sciences formed a committee of experts to investigate the problem, and to evaluate and coordinate the rash of studies being conducted by organizations and scientists scattered across the land, and the federal government established an Interagency Task Force on Inadvertent Modification of the Stratosphere. In June, the Task Force, convinced of the potential threat of fluorocarbons, recommended banning aerosol sprays employing those gases by January 1978, "unless new evidence is found to remove the cause for concern."

All of the studies, committees and investigations were necessary because so few hard facts were available. There was little evidence about the degree of pollution of the stratosphere or about the effect this pollution might have on the atmosphere's ozone shield. Only in 1973 did anyone begin to measure fluorocarbon levels in the stratosphere, and the recordings thus far are too few and cover too short a time span to indicate how serious the problem really is.

The ozone concentration has been measured at different locations over many decades (by

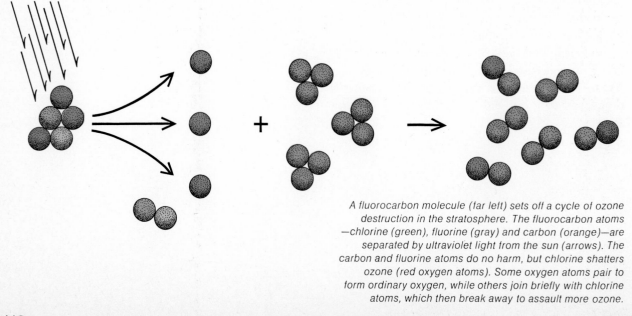

A fluorocarbon molecule (far left) sets off a cycle of ozone destruction in the stratosphere. The fluorocarbon atoms —chlorine (green), fluorine (gray) and carbon (orange)—are separated by ultraviolet light from the sun (arrows). The carbon and fluorine atoms do no harm, but chlorine shatters ozone (red oxygen atoms). Some oxygen atoms pair to form ordinary oxygen, while others join briefly with chlorine atoms, which then break away to assault more ozone.

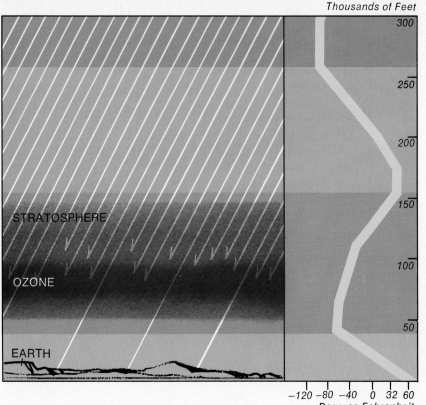

300

250

200

150

STRATOSPHERE

100

OZONE

50

EARTH

−120 −80 −40 0 32 60
Degrees Fahrenheit

Changes of temperature in the stratosphere (plotted in the graph) trap fluorocarbons where they deplete the ozone layer (gray band) and reduce its ability to block out ultraviolet rays (diagonal lines). Below the stratosphere, temperature decreases with increasing altitude. But in the stratosphere, absorption of ultraviolet raises temperature, forming a layer of warm air, or "inversion," that keeps cool air—and contaminants— below from rising and dissipating.

gauging the solar radiation that reaches ground level), and it is known to vary from time to time and place to place. It appears to have decreased over the years between 1970 and 1974 by perhaps 2 per cent—a change, but this change is blamed on random variations caused by natural phenomena (not only does the ozone supply vary seasonally, but it is also thought to be affected by an 11-year sunspot cycle). Yet there is enough indirect evidence for concern.

The quantity of fluorocarbon in the troposphere, i.e., the lower atmosphere, not the ozone-containing stratosphere, has increased dramatically, as might be expected from the boom in the use of spray cans and other sources. Measurements at sea level in the East Pacific by the Naval Research Laboratory showed the concentration was 35 per cent higher in February 1974 than it was in November 1972, and a considerable amount of it continually drifts up into the stratosphere. There are still only about 80 parts per trillion in the lower atmosphere, but even this small amount of a synthetic gas might bring drastic results, as demonstrated by laboratory experiments at four universities: California, Pittsburgh, Pennsylvania State and Maryland. In some tests, when fluorocarbon gases in glass containers were exposed to ultraviolet lamps, free chlorine was indeed released. In other experiments, free chlorine was mixed with ozone, and the ozone indeed was broken down.

Much in dispute is the one significant question arising from the latter group of experiments: What is the rate at which ozone is destroyed and then reconstituted? This rate determines the potential danger. But most scientists agree that the processes observed in the laboratory also occur in the stratosphere, that this ozone destruction could be accelerated by increasing contamination, and that a decrease in ozone would have damaging effects on the earth below.

The most dangerous consequence for human health would probably be a rise in skin cancer brought on by increased ultraviolet radiation (the two most common forms are treatable if caught in time and, though they can be painful, are generally nonfatal; the third, rarer cancer, malignant melanoma, can spread rapidly through the body

Not only spray-can fluorocarbons, but also exhaust fumes from supersonic aircraft like the Anglo-French Concorde will react with ozone. A report from the U.S. Department of Transportation released last February finally concluded, after four years of debate, that SSTs might deplete the earth's ozone layer if large numbers take to the air.

and in about 40 per cent of recorded cases has proved a cause of death). Studies in the United States show that the incidence of skin cancer varies geographically, with those people living nearer the equator more likely to suffer than those living farther north. This reflects the fact that the ozone layer increases in thickness away from the equator and toward the poles, filtering more ultraviolet from sunlight in those latitudes.

According to a 1974 survey by the National Cancer Institute, the Dallas area has about four cases per 1,000 persons of the two common skin cancers, squamous cell carcinoma and basal cell carcinoma; the Minneapolis area, some 900 miles north and shielded by 30 per cent more ozone, reported less than half that number: 1.5 cases per 1,000. Though projections vary, a 5 per cent ozone decrease could boost skin cancer figures by about 10 per cent, causing some 30,000 additional cases a year in the United States and perhaps as many as a half-million cases worldwide. The increase would strike the fair-skinned one third of the world's population most directly; black-, brown- and yellow-skinned races receive considerable protection from their pigmentation.

A significant decrease in ozone, increasing ultraviolet exposure, could also heighten bodily reactions to various chemical agents, such as certain antibiotics and tranquilizers and antibacterial soaps and cosmetics. In addition, it could cause a higher rate of eye injuries, particularly in regions where radiation is brightly reflected from large areas of sand, water, snow or ice. And though ultraviolet light is beneficial in stimulating the bodily production of vitamin D, which is essential to man and other bony animals, an excess of the vitamin can be toxic.

There are other sobering possibilities that

could affect man indirectly but severely through the ecosystems on which he depends. Ultraviolet rays can kill harmful bacteria and for this reason are often used in sterilizing lamps. But they can also kill beneficial bacteria and other small organisms like algae, diatoms and zooplankton, which form the base of aquatic food chains; a major ultraviolet increase could thus have profound effects on world fisheries and the animals and humans who depend on them.

On land, experiments have shown that increased ultraviolet radiation leads to stunting, tumors and mutations in plants, particularly in the more sensitive agricultural species. Changes in solar radiation could also have far-reaching effects on the behavior of those insects whose vision extends beyond that of man into the ultraviolet range, possibly interfering with their flying and navigation systems, flower recognition and nectar clues—and even their communication and procreation (many butterflies are thought to recognize potential mates by the bright flashes, invisible to the human eye, from ultraviolet-reflecting areas on their wings).

Until such frightening speculations inspired a flurry of headlines, most people had little cause to think about the stratosphere or its ultraviolet-blocking ozone layer. Ozone is a close relative of the ordinary oxygen that animals breathe to live, except that ozone molecules consist of three atoms instead of the two in ordinary oxygen. Ozone is formed when strong sunlight (or an electrical discharge) splits ordinary oxygen molecules and some of the resulting atoms recombine in threes rather than in twos. Ozone can sometimes be noticed by its pungent smell near electrical machinery and power lines, or in the air right after a lightning storm; it is also a by-product of sunlight acting on city smog, and in this role is a familiar irritant to the eyes.

Ozone exists in the stratosphere because, up there, the sun's unshielded rays begin a regular cycle of ozone formation and destruction: The rays break down ordinary oxygen molecules, allowing the formation of scattered ozone molecules—which are, in their turn, destroyed by naturally produced nitrogen oxides arising from decaying matter on earth.

This layer of ozone is incredibly tenuous—it forms only one millionth of the atmosphere's total mass. But since it plays such a crucial role in moderating those solar rays most destructive to nucleic acids and proteins, the building blocks of living cells in plants and animals, this thin screen is a vital protection. Scientists generally agree that life on dry land would have been impossible without it.

THE PRIMORDIAL OZONE
Ozone was probably absent when life originally began on earth and, paradoxically, its very absence contributed to the initial formation of life. The atmosphere then contained few free oxygen molecules of any kind, and powerful radiation from the sun poured onto the primordial seas and pools, stimulating the genesis of complex compounds that came to exhibit the characteristics of living things. These borderline substances evolved into plants, with the ability to live by photosynthesis: They used the sunlight to convert nutrients into food. In the process, they released waste products, among which was free oxygen. Gradually the primitive plants' waste oxygen built up in the atmosphere until enough filtered up into the stratosphere to be converted into ozone.

Not until some 400 million years ago, when there was enough ozone to provide some protection from the ultraviolet radiation, did plants begin to evolve land-based forms and create the environment later to be colonized by animals. Without the emergence of this thin stratospheric shield, animal life—humans included—could never have come along. If the ozone layer vanished, or was seriously damaged, life might be forced into an irreversible decline.

The ozone layer is peculiarly susceptible to damage, mainly because of two closely related characteristics of the stratosphere: its temperature pattern and its stability, in both of which it forms a sharp contrast to the troposphere below (graph, page 117). In the troposphere, which is generally cooler above and warmer below, falling cold air and rising warm air create constant turbulence and condensation that act like a huge, efficient washing machine, cleansing the lower atmosphere of many of its impurities.

The stratosphere acts in quite the opposite way. It absorbs high-energy radiation more in its upper levels than in its lower ones, and is consequently in a permanent state of temperature inversion, a condition in which hot air remains stagnantly above cold air, preventing vertical mixing. In an inversion, the air moves mainly in sandwich-like horizontal layers, spreading out in what meteorologists call the pancake effect. (This sometimes occurs on the earth's surface. When it happens over an industrial area enclosed between hills—as Los Angeles is—the result is smog that thickens until the inversion is reversed by a weather shift.) This static layering means that any impurities that are carried up into the stratosphere tend to remain there a very long time, diffusing slowly outward and around the earth before they finally drift out into space.

Since most chemicals rising from the earth are reactive or water-soluble, they are caught in the troposphere's cloud-and-rain filter and washed back to earth. Those that are inert or insoluble, however, may escape the tropospheric trap and reach the stratosphere, spreading horizontally and remaining there for years, possibly to deplete the ozone layer and increase the amount of ultraviolet radiation reaching the earth.

This is what the ozone debate is all about. It became increasingly apparent that pinning down all the pollutants—and all the possible causes of trouble—was not going to be an easy matter. The scare over stratospheric pollution, in fact, was first raised not by fluorocarbon spray cans but by supersonic air transports (SSTs). As far back as 1970, a few scientists worried that the huge planes, cruising through the stratosphere, could release in their exhausts quantities of nitric oxide, adding to the supply from natural sources, known to be the principal regulator of ozone in the stratosphere.

Nitric oxide, which consists of one molecule of nitrogen and one of oxygen, can attack ozone in two successive ways: First it snatches one atom of oxygen from one molecule of ozone to produce nitrogen dioxide and ordinary oxygen; then the nitrogen dioxide briefly combines with another atom of free oxygen—which will not then be available for the formation of ozone—before

dividing in two as a molecule of oxygen and a molecule of nitric oxide. The nitric oxide thus acts as a catalyst: It initiates a reaction that destroys ozone, but allows the nitric oxide to emerge unscathed, ready to start the same set of reactions all over again. One molecule of nitric oxide thus can go on gobbling up ozone until it finally drifts out of the ozone layer.

The scientist who first spread the alarm was Harold Johnston, Professor of Chemistry at the University of California at Berkeley; in 1971 he calculated that 500 SSTs flying 13 miles up for seven hours a day over a period of 10 years would dump enough nitric oxide aloft to deplete the world's layer of ozone by 22 per cent. During the emotion-charged wrangling that surrounded the SST issue, Congress in 1971 discontinued subsidies for the development of SSTs.

Though the original estimates have been severely criticized—projections of the timing, size and engine power of an SST fleet were probably overly generous, and Johnston admittedly used a primitive model for his calculations—the eventual possibility of American SSTs, and the continuing development of the French-English Concorde and Russian Tupolev supersonic craft, led Congress to direct the U.S. Department of Transportation to establish the Climatic Impact Assessment Program (CIAP), a four-year, $20-million-plus study. None of its findings, published in 1975, refuted the early theories in principle, despite some confusions and misunderstandings that crept into the press. CIAP saw little immediate danger in the present handful of Concordes and TU-144s. Larger fleets of several hundred supersonics, and increasing numbers of high-flying subsonic jetliners, however, would indeed pose a very real problem.

SURPRISES KEEP COMING

Even as CIAP was developing data on SSTs, the new interest in the stratosphere led to the discovery, largely accidental, of other threats. In considering nitric-oxide emissions from high-flying aircraft, Harold Johnston and Julius Chang of the Lawrence Livermore Laboratory at Berkeley realized that the tremendous heat of atomic explosions, by causing oxygen and nitrogen mol-

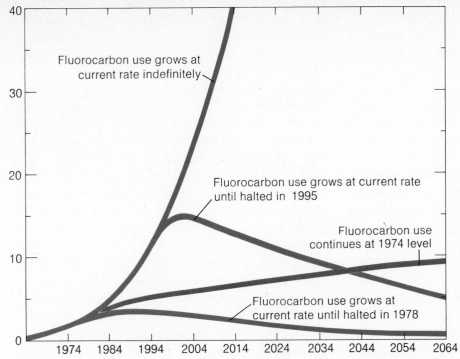

Fluorocarbon use grows at current rate indefinitely

Fluorocarbon use grows at current rate until halted in 1995

Fluorocarbon use continues at 1974 level

Fluorocarbon use grows at current rate until halted in 1978

Among these four estimates of the impact of fluorocarbons on ozone in the earth's atmosphere, the worst (top gray line) assumes that our use of fluorocarbons will continue to increase at its present annual rate of 10 per cent. In this unlikely event, almost half the vital ozone layer would vanish in 50 years. Lesser estimates, which assume cutbacks in production, foresee depletions ranging from 14 per cent to an insignificant 3 per cent.

ecules in the air to combine, could produce in an instant more nitric oxide than a whole fleet of SSTs and could carry it rapidly aloft into the stratosphere. A full-scale nuclear exchange between the United States and Soviet Russia, it was estimated, might reduce the amount of ozone by 50 per cent or more, exposing whatever life is left on earth to a slow death.

The second—and even more insidious—surprise was the discovery that something else in the air might be still more efficient in attacking the ozone layer than nitric oxide from SSTs or nuclear holocausts. Three groups of scientists working on the SST problem—at the University of Michigan, at Harvard, and the National Center for Atmospheric Research at Boulder, Colorado—began to wonder what other vehicles might possibly pollute the stratosphere. They soon realized that one, at least, had already been sanctioned: the space shuttle, a reusable rocket that by 1979 would act as a ferry between earth and orbiting space stations *(Nature/Science Annual 1973, Building Laboratories in the Sky— page 30).* With the space shuttle, the problem was not nitric oxide, but chlorine, one of the chemicals that would be produced when the

shuttle's exhaust was broken down by solar radiation. It was already known that chlorine could destroy ozone six times more effectively than nitric oxide. In a similar two-stage catalytic reaction *(diagram, page 116),* each atom of chlorine first breaks up a molecule of ozone to form a chlorine compound, which thereupon reacts with more oxygen to re-create free chlorine, which starts the ozone-destroying process all over again. In this way a single chlorine molecule could, it is estimated, destroy as many as 100,000 ozone molecules before its activity ended. But in late 1973, having pointed out the possible danger, scientists decided that everyone, in effect, could sit back and relax because there was as yet no major source of chlorine up there.

Or was there? Sherwood Rowland and his colleague Mario Molina at the University of California at Irvine, working along lines unconnected with the space shuttle, set about tracing what could happen to fluorocarbons after they had escaped into the atmosphere. Rowland, a specialist in the chemistry of radioactive atoms, had been bothered by the problem since 1972, after fluorocarbons had been detected in the air, from samples taken as far apart as Norway and South

America. Since the compounds were known to be inert, no one had worried; in fact scientists had welcomed them as possible tracers when they charted wind patterns.

CLUES—AND CONCERNS—MOUNT

But Rowland was concerned, and remained so for the next three years. The United States fluorocarbon industry was huge, and growing at a rate variously estimated at between 10 per cent and 20 per cent per year. In 1973 its output was valued at $500 million, of which $250 million went into spray cans. Much of the rest went into refrigerants, which circulate through home freezers, air conditioners and large-scale cooling systems, in a heat-exchanging cycle of expansion and contraction. It is quite difficult to manufacture systems that are leakproof; considerable amounts of coolant are sold to "top off" large cooling devices and automobile air conditioners. And even the best-sealed systems can leak when junked. Other possible sources of fluorocarbon contamination were the smaller but growing market for the compounds used as solvents for cleaning electronic circuits, as raw materials for making plastics and as agents to puff up plastics, like the foamed material used in insulation, packaging, furniture stuffing and disposable cups.

Finally, the burgeoning use of fluorocarbons was not just an American phenomenon; since the basic patents expired over 20 years ago, other manufacturers around the world have been producing these compounds. Among them they now make a million tons annually, about half of which originates outside the United States.

Rowland and Molina reasoned that fluorocarbons, because of their high stability, could not be eliminated by the natural "sinks" that take care of other chemicals: They could not be dissolved in the oceans, absorbed by other particles, converted to new compounds by other chemicals or dissolved by rainwater. Since almost all the fluorocarbons ever made—amounting to several million tons—were presumably still floating about, calculations showed that considerable amounts could already have diffused up into the stratosphere, and the effects of the resultant chlorine could already be considerable.

These calculations led to others of cataclysmic portent. If fluorocarbon production continued unabated, according to one estimate, as much as 14 per cent of the ozone layer might be gone by the year 2000, with correspondingly severe consequences for life on earth. Such figures have since been challenged, and the principal researchers in the field are still seeking to establish the rate at which the known reactions occur by varying the experimental conditions in the laboratory to match the varying conditions that exist in the stratosphere. "What we are trying to do," says Michael McElroy, a leading atmospheric scientist at Harvard University, "is to get a total picture of the ozone problem, and we think that fluorocarbons are only a part of it. They are an indication, a warning that subtle uses of modern technology can have serious effects on the environment. I think we have yet to see the picture in its entire scope."

A major attempt to grasp the scope of the problem has begun, in the field as well as in the lab, by determining at what rate various chemicals diffuse upward into the stratosphere. During 1975 the federal government's Energy Research and Development Administration will send a specially equipped airplane on three separate three-week-long missions, to fly along the west coast of the Americas from north of Alaska to Peru, collecting air samples in the lower atmosphere. In addition, the National Center for Atmospheric Research is launching the first of a series of unmanned balloons, half of which will go as high as 28 miles. And in early 1975 a satellite, already in orbit as a miniature astronomical observatory, was programed to scan for the presence of chlorine molecules in the ozone layer.

Only when the complex and continuing work has produced a sizable body of hard data will scientists know what, if anything, ought to be done. According to most estimates, the evaluation will take at least two years, and probably three or more, and in the meantime more than one of the scientists is working with a sense of urgency. As McElroy says: "If it took us four years to discover all those previously unsuspected things up there in the air, what else has managed to slip by?"

Two balloons like this one, ready for an early test flight, took off in June to sample fluorocarbon levels in the stratosphere. Part of a long-range investigation, the balloons will provide actual data on stratospheric pollutants.

Boy in a Plastic Cocoon

The contented four-month-old below never has felt the comforting warmth of direct human contact, from his mother or anyone else. Young David (his family name is withheld by the hospital) has spent his life sealed in plastic cocoons, lest his inborn inability to resist infection—a rare defect called agammaglobulinemia—quickly make him prey to germs. Despite this total isolation, the love of his mother and dozens of substitute parents apparently has transcended the sterile shield and is helping him grow up well adjusted. David ranks normal or better by every psychological measurement, and his doctors say he is emotionally more mature than most children his age. His vocabulary is remarkably adult, reflecting a lifelong association with scientists. David's progress surprises many psychologists, for skin-to-skin mothering has been considered important to normal development.

In all but one respect David may be the health-

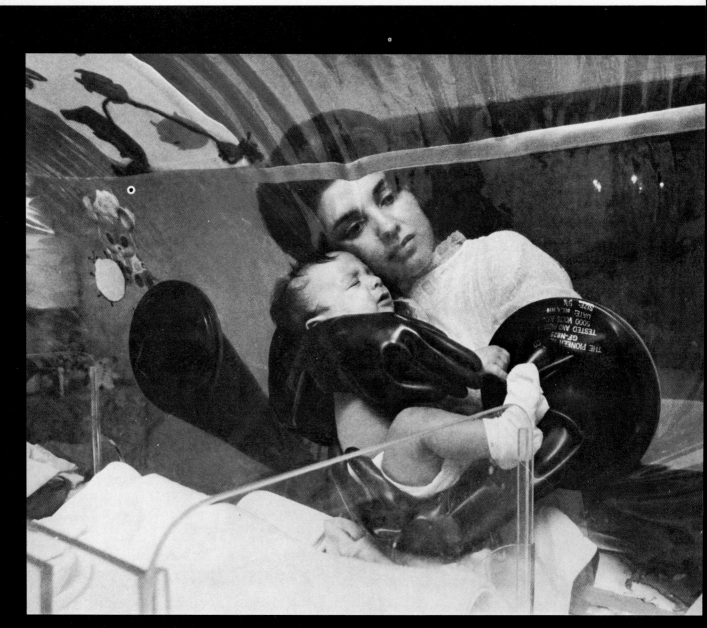

iest person on earth. He has never been sick and is protected from the swarms of bacteria that everyone else combats each moment. David's isolation began the moment he was born, at Texas Children's Hospital in Houston, lacking two immunological systems that develop naturally in all but one in 10,000 babies. One defense is provided by gamma globulin, a blood substance that contains antibodies against disease; the second system depends on another blood component, specialized white cells called lymphocytes, which attack infectious invaders directly. Doctors had suspected that David would suffer from agammaglobulinemia. His mother had given birth the year before to a son who had died as a result of the same genetic deficiency. So when David arrived, a team of doctors was in attendance for what may have been the most sterile birth in history. The baby was placed immediately in the first of his many germ-free isolators.

David did not seem to be aware of his imprisonment until about the time of his third birthday. On a visit home, while watching his father do some chores, David said, "You let me out of this bubble and I'll help you." Later he told his mother, "When I get out of this bubble, I'll go with you to the kitchen." They were natural, offhand remarks—but carried ominous implications. The doctors say that the youngster is smart enough to break out of his life-protecting isolation if he

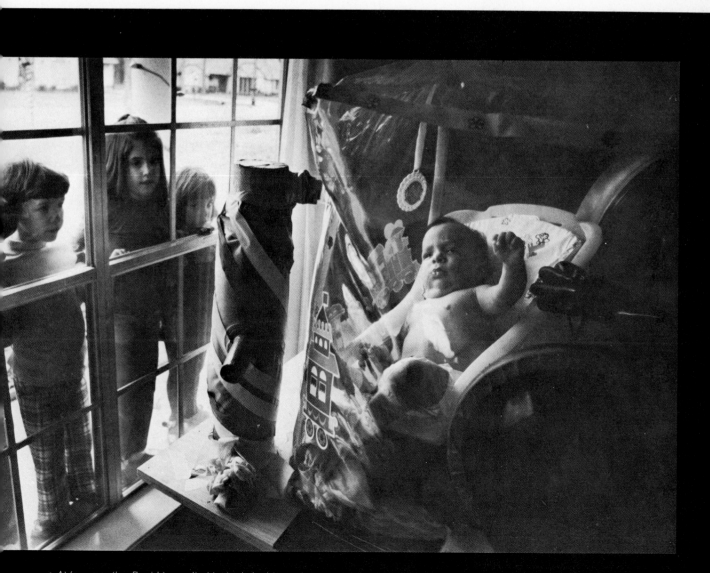

◄ At four months, David is cradled lovingly by his mother (left) despite a barrier of plastic and gloves that guard him against disease bacteria that his body cannot resist. She has never been able to touch him directly.

David wriggles inside his germ-free bubble (above), watched by three of 20 neighbor children who often play with him on visits home. Sterilized air is pumped

wishes. They hope that David's yen for freedom can be contained until they devise a safe way to expose him to the outside.

Two approaches have been considered. One is a child-sized astronaut's suit, designed by NASA engineers, to provide a mobile version of the sealed cocoon. The other approach depends on tantalizing but inconclusive research that may cure David's deficiency, freeing him for good.

So far, attempts to remedy his ailment have been disheartening. After he was born, doctors considered transplanting bone marrow from a normal human. Marrow contains "seed" cells that ordinarily stimulate the body to produce germ-fighting white blood cells. Transplanted marrow might induce David's blood-cell system to start working—if it came from someone whose marrow "matched" David's own; nonmatching marrow cells would probably kill him. Unfortunately, none of David's 20 blood relatives has matching bone marrow and the odds against finding anyone who does are 32,000 to one.

The medical experts also considered two other transplant operations. The fetal liver, which restores seed cells, and the thymus gland, which can turn on these seed cells, each can help enhance immunity to disease and, for uncertain reasons, both transplants take fairly readily. However, tests with David's blood and body tissue showed that neither one would improve his disease resistance, nor would a hormone called thymosin, which has helped other children less

At three years, David climbs into a toy turtle in his plastic playroom as his scientist-godfather, Dr. Raphael Wilson watches (above). Because David is sensitive to moods of others, Dr. Wilson decorated the area to cheer up visitors.

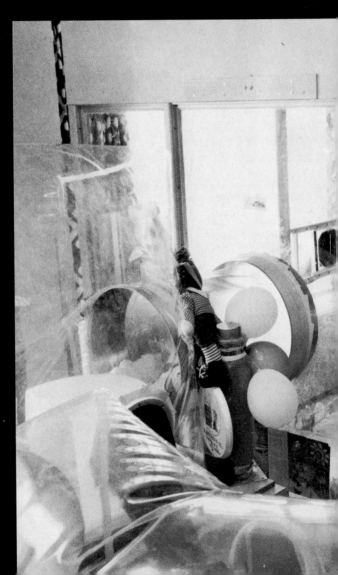

David explores the open space of a bigger playroom. Earlier he had lived in small isolators like those in foreground. He alternates between sealed bubbles at home or in the hospital, traveling from one to another in a portable isolator

severely affected with the deficiency. In 1975, research by a number of microbiologists, including David's godmother, Dr. Patricia Bealmear of Baylor College of Medicine, Houston, offered new hope. She has developed a serum that appears to block the mechanism that usually causes nonmatching marrow transplants to kill the patient. It has worked on some experimental animals and may work on David if his parents and doctors decide the risk is acceptable.

Meanwhile, David remains trapped in his safe, plastic world, but he is no longer entirely bacteria-free. Seven harmless bacteria have been deliberately introduced into his intestines, to help break down food and extract its nutrients. David's diet of bottled baby foods, transferred into his bubbles via sterilized containers, is carefully regulated. He is stronger and taller than most boys his age and even though he often selects dessert for breakfast and dinner for lunch, he consistently ends each day with a balanced diet, without prompting.

No one knows what effects continued confinement might have on David's personality. David has generally been a happy, outgoing child who chatters constantly with doctors, nurses and parents. "There is no child alive in the world today who has had so thorough a study, nutritionally, neurologically, psychologically and physically," says Dr. Raphael Wilson, "yet he's a very happy child who has a good relationship with everyone. We are very hopeful of getting him out safely."

DON A. SCHANCHE

A miniature space suit, demonstrated here by the daughter of the NASA engineer who helped design it, may enable David to move around on his own outside his bubbles. Batteries on the lawn-mower carriage behind him supply power to pump germless air into his suit for up to four hours at a time. However, this clumsy substitute for normal freedom may prove unnecessary: medical advances may offer a cure for David's rare susceptibility to germs.

The Switch to Metrics

THE METERS AND LITERS ARE COMING, AMID CONFUSION

It was a small item, half hidden in the business pages of the newspapers on December 10, 1974, but it signaled the beginning of an era. The federal government ruled that, after January 1, 1979, wine must be bottled in liters and fractions of liters. The United States was, finally, firmly on its way to adopting the metric system of measures that is standard everywhere else in the world except Burma, Brunei, Liberia and Yemen. Under the metric system, kilometers, meters and centimeters replace miles, yards, feet and inches; liters replace gallons and quarts; kilograms replace pounds; Celsius (or Centigrade) degrees replace Fahrenheit.

The order was official confirmation of a trend that has been accelerating in recent years. In 1971 IBM began making all new products to metric specifications. In 1973 a brand-new Ford plant in Lima, Ohio, started turning out metric engines for Pintos and Mustangs. And in 1975 supermarkets received their first shipments of 7-UP in liter and half-liter bottles.

In a world that uses Japanese television sets, German cars, Scotch whisky, Korean cigarette lighters, and American jet airplanes, one universal system of measures is not only a convenience but a necessity. Understandably, the greatest pressure in the United States for "metrication" has come from industry, which counts on selling $110 billion worth of goods a year to people who measure in meters. But while the reasons for a change to metric measures may lie overseas, the most pronounced effects will be felt at home.

For simplicity, the metric system is the best ever devised. It eliminates oddball units: perches, furlongs, chains and links, wagonloads, jacks and gills, to say nothing of the Philadelphia foot, which is longer than the United States foot and lingers in land records to this day. It ends the complexity of converting measures. Who remembers how many gills there are in a pint? Or how many feet in a mile? (There were 5,000 feet in a mile until Queen Elizabeth I confused everybody but horseplayers by making a mile 5,280 feet, so it would equal exactly eight furlongs.)

No longer will it be necessary to say something is 4 yards 2 feet 10 inches long, or weighs 5 pounds 13 ounces. Metric units are decimal: 10 millimeters to the centimeter, 100 centimeters to the meter, 1,000 meters to the kilometer. Thus an object measuring 4 meters 25 centimeters 6 millimeters is simply 4.256 meters long—or 425.6 centimeters. The advantage is overwhelming when measures are added, multiplied or divided.

Logically and rationally, the metric system seems to be the answer to the prayers of the man who has never been able to measure a window accurately enough for his wife's curtains. Psychologically, it may not be. Most people boggle at decimals. No one ever asks the butcher for .25 pound of bologna, or even 4 ounces of bologna; it is always a 1/4 pound. Besides, the metric system, for all its neat interrelationships, lacks some handy units. It contains nothing like the foot, which is about the length of an average man's shoe, enabling him to step off distances quite accurately. Whether such disadvantages are real or imaginary is hotly disputed by the authorities. Yet they seem very real and important to a great many people, as Paul O'Neil explains (overleaf) in an article about the trials of the world's conversion—past and future—to metrics.

Highway workers erect the first U.S. road sign to specify metric distances, on Interstate 71 between Columbus and Cleveland. By placing such dual distance signs, officials hope to prepare the public for gradual metric changeover.

The Rocky Road to Litersville

by Paul O'Neil

With the rapid changeover to the metric system, all sorts of big U.S. corporations have begun to squint, shudder and gulp down doses of "metrication"—an expensive and odd-tasting panacea with curious side effects, but one now regarded as the only antibiotic that can keep American industry healthy in an overwhelmingly metric world. In consequence, the federal government is about to advance upon the rest of us and to say—with spoon in hand: "Open up. This stuff is good for you, too." Don't think we won't swallow—at least in the end.

But an awful lot of us are going to squirm and wonder—even as we are being told how much better we will feel when we learn to buy carrots by the kilogram—if something that is good for the owner of the medicine show is necessarily good for us. The process by which metric weights and measures will supplant our present standards is going to be a much more complicated affair than its advocates may now imagine.

The metric system was conceived by scientists for scientists as a means of 1) wiping a miserable fungus of bucolic guesswork from the works of civilized man, and of 2) presenting the world with an elegant and integrated system of standards based on one immutable and fundamental "natural" measurement—one ten millionth of the meridional quadrant of the earth (or Great Circle distance between the equator and the pole) that lies just west of Paris.

Its authors were motivated by the attitudes of European "Enlightenment." The 17th and 18th century leaders of this age of rationalism challenged the Western world's basic reliance on myth and established custom, and believed that man should turn to reason and nature in seeking freedom and happiness. The metric system reflected both these means of "progress toward perfection" and its promoters believed it would wipe away feudal (and overlapping) concepts of measurement and prove a mighty pillar of their brave, new, ever-more-rational world.

A twelve-man committee of the French Academy of Sciences called the system's basic lineal measure a *metron* (Greek for measure) and provided it with Greek and Latin multiples and submultiples. Nothing was allowed to impede its implementation: The Bastille had fallen and French revolutionaries were panting to demolish every attitude and practice of the *ancien régime*.

Two astronomers, Jean Delambre and Pierre Méchain were sent off, posthaste, to measure the meridional distance from Barcelona to Dunkirk and thus secure geodetic evidence upon which to base the meter-to-be (though not, curiously, before a committee of their colleagues visited Louis XVI in prison and obtained his authorization for the project). But wonderful irony now intruded upon the scientists: Their techniques, as things turned out, were incapable of really mastering nature and the meter had to be derived from a process that was almost—if not quite—as arbitrary as had been the medieval rite of measuring the king's foot.

Delambre and Méchain had a terrible time—if only because they were forced to dodge armies that kept fighting across the terrain they were trying to survey—and did not finish their arduous work for six long years. Scientists in Paris set out, in the interim, to contrive a *provisional* meter, using what imperfect geodetic data they found already at hand.

FINE MEASUREMENTS OF THE EARTH

The rest of the metric system was devised, also provisionally, on the basis of their work: the liter was defined as the volume of a 10-centimeter cube, the gram as the mass of a cubic centimeter of pure water at 4° C. (its temperature of greatest density), and the hectare as 10,000 square meters. And there the matter rested for many years, with hopes of final correction obscured by critics who charged that the work of Delambre and Méchain was shot with error and that surveying techniques of the day simply could not yield fine enough measurements of the earth.

Engineers constructed a measured platinum rod (a Metre of the Archives) and a platinum cylinder (a Kilogram of the Archives), and the metric system—having been adopted by law in 1795—was ordained as the official standard of France in 1799. It served science and engineering beautifully because its decimal mathematics and its logically interrelated concepts of mass, capacity and area were unaffected by the meter's relationship—accurate or inaccurate—to larger aspects of the planet. The meter is still the length of that platinum rod, but the rod's length can today be related to a natural dimension, a 20th Century's fulfillment of the 18th Century's hope. The meter is now defined as 1,650,763.73 wave lengths in vacuum of the orange-red line of the spectrum of the rare gas called krypton-86.

Americans began weighing the adoption of the new standards almost as soon as they were conceived. Thomas Jefferson was fascinated with the idea of the meter (although he thought the Frenchmen could have saved themselves a great deal of work by basing it on the natural swing of a pendulum). So was John Quincy Adams. He thought the new system "worthy of acceptance without question," and one, furthermore, that "concealed no lurking danger to independence . . . no *ultima ratio* of cannon balls." But he also noted that public opinion "is queen of the world" and stated with some regret that the country was not ready to accept it. Or—he might have added—any other Gallic idea. Americans of the period were appalled at French revolutionaries—whom they had earlier admired as brothers in democracy—for their ugly tendency to chop off other Frenchmen's heads.

One thing is certain: metric conversion would have been a great deal simpler in the early 1800s than it is likely to be in the 1970s and 1980s. Most Congressional exponents of metrics believe that its costs must be allowed, as in England, to "lie where they fall"—that the government must not attempt to predict or defray expenses but should leave business in the toils of necessity to make changes as quickly and cheaply as possible. Both organized labor and small business reject this thesis and any national metric board that Congress creates to adjudicate the problems of conversion must prepare itself for cries of protest and outrage from both sides.

MACHINISTS AND METRICATION

The case for Labor—which is most vociferously voiced by the International Brotherhood of Electrical Workers and the International Association of Machinists and Aerospace Workers—involves a coony hope of exacting free metric hand tools from the government. Labor, in general, has a horrible suspicion that metrication may cost jobs; that it will disrupt the craft seniority system (since downy-faced apprentices learn metrics faster than grizzled journeymen) and that talk of industrial isolation is "grossly misleading" anyhow—since the "U.S. industrial giant still represents a third of total world production."

The machinists, in particular, are concentrating on free replacement tools (for the men who traditionally bring their own to the job) and have drawn up a list worth about $2,000 per man that it is hoped the taxpayer will provide. This union has insisted for years that employers replace lost or stolen micrometers, gauges and calipers and will certainly—if all else fails—ask for metric replacements at the bargaining table.

The nation's small businessmen—and particularly 400,000 of them who make up the National Federation of Independent Business—have even darker forebodings.

"A lot of these people," says their voluble, pink-faced lobbyist John J. Motley, "are running groceries and garages and hardware stores. They have nothing to do with international trade, but when a company like General Motors and its 40,000 suppliers start going metric the little guy is going to be caught up in it too, sooner or later. Take those big, white scales the butcher uses; it's going to cost an awful lot of money—something like $1,000—to replace or convert them. We'll need help. We have 40,000 small manufacturers who are going to be worse off. They get small bites of government contracts now because the law and the Small Business Administration say small bites have to be set aside for them. But agencies such as the Pentagon like big companies and big contracts and they'd like

Working with this ornate theodolite —a double-telescope device used for precise distance measurement— 18th Century French astronomers Delambre and Méchain set out to establish the size of the standard meter. They measured one ten millionth of a quadrant of the earth's surface, and this length was used in making a platinum-iridium bar still preserved at Sèvres in France. However, the standard of length is now specified by wavelengths of light emitted from the gas krypton (opposite).

The standard for all metric weights, since 1799 has been the innocuous-looking International Kilogram, which reposes under three dust-proof glass domes at the International Bureau of Weights and Measures in Sèvres. Made from a platinum-iridium alloy, it equals a cubic decimeter of water in weight. This kilogram is handled only with the velvet-lined tongs lying nearby—even a fingerprint could alter its precise weight.

The meter, now defined by the number ▶ of wavelengths of the gas krypton-86, may soon be measured in wavelengths of laser light. A yellow helium-neon laser beam (upper left) is reflected up into an interferometer, a precise measuring device, together with the bluish beam (right) from a mercury lamp. The interferometer compares the two beams to determine the laser's wavelength. Once that is known, scientists can count the number of laser lengths in a meter—and thus duplicate it quickly and accurately.

an excuse to forget the little guy; our fellows are afraid they'll lose out if they can't convert to metrics on time. We want subsidies to help them do it. Congress is saying, 'No,' but we get subsidies to help us comply with other government orders —on pollution for instance—and we don't see that metrics will be any different.''

Managers of the biggest U.S. corporations, even those multinational firms with a real stake in metrication, would be happier today, too, if they could avoid the expense and turmoil that are about to be visited upon them; but a tremendous amount of painstaking and intelligent conversion planning is underway, nevertheless, in board rooms and drafting offices of such companies. Big labor—though preparing to fight for what it can get from conversion—is resigned to the inevitable. Unions and employers have long since joined forces, in fact, to establish and finance an American National Metric Council as a counterbalance to metric management by government. This ANMC produces guidance pamphlets by the score and it sponsors technical seminars, coast to coast, in such diverse settings as the Washington Hilton Hotel, Alabama's Redstone Arsenal and the American Inn near O'Hare Airport in Chicago.

But none of this means that big firms, too, will not find themselves plagued by quandaries when they fully commit themselves to so vast a program of industrial change. Although the major corporations are better able than small ones to write off the considerable expense that will be entailed in conversion, they will fall prey, by their very size, to difficulty in 1) exacting a smooth flow of new metric parts from thousands of struggling suppliers, 2) producing and maintaining inventories of old-fashioned parts for equipment already sold and in use, and 3) making a simultaneous attempt to simplify their products and manufacturing processes and thus wrench new efficiency and profit from the ordeal to which they are submitting.

We need only consider the part that nuts, bolts, screws, rivets, washers and cotter pins will play in this convulsive attempt at self-betterment. More than three and a half million separate and distinct kinds, shapes and sizes of such lowly

''fasteners'' are used in United States manufacturing today—55 per cent of the cost of labor in 22 major industries is devoted, in fact, to sticking them into machinery of every conceivable kind. Labeling fasteners in metric terms would be a dizzying enough project, but creating new ones to an international standard will be more confusing yet, for Europe has not one but ten metric systems for fasteners—none of which, thanks to military suspicion, is interchangeable with another—and all of these, too, must be sorted out, through a process of technical diplomacy, before the goals of multinational manufacturers are, at last, achieved.

IN ENGLAND: METRIC BRUSSELS SPROUTS

It is the United States consumer, of course, upon whom the fallout from these mushroom clouds of industrial dilemma will eventually descend; thus we can only peer in fascination at his counterpart in England—which began its conversion program in 1965, but has yet to convince the man in the street that metric clothes, metric cars and metric Brussels sprouts are really keys to the better life. The man in Piccadilly Circus seemed only certain, on the approach of M (for Metric) Day that shopkeepers were going to use the differences between metric and customary weights to steal the gold out of his teeth, as he was equally certain they had done by raising prices on D (for Disaster) Day when the cumbersome English monetary system was decimalized at last. ''Purposeless change'' wrote a reader of the London *Times,* ''which eats away at the character!'' A *Daily Mail* editorial seconded this view: ''They cannot tolerate our glorious profusion of measures which fit in, not with some bureaucrat's mental slide rule, but with the human body. A foot is a foot . . . a pint is a gulletful.''

In many cases shopkeepers and small tradesmen seemed fully as repelled by metrics as were their suspicious customers. When a survey was taken recently, managers of small building firms in Sussex and Surrey—who had refused to take available metric training courses for six years —displayed attitudes that ranged from ''amused tolerance to . . . apparent defiance.'' London butchers announced that they would not go met-

A decimal pocket watch is a rare reminder of an ill-fated attempt to include time measurements in the metric system. In 1793 the French government promulgated a day of 20 hours with divisions of 100 minutes and 100 seconds. The decimal time scheme fell into disuse after a few years.

ric unless forced to do so by law and that they would refuse to comply even then if their costs were not borne by the government. Fishmongers and greengrocers also balked at converting. "I'll think about it when it 'appens," said a cockney stallholder as he stolidly weighed out a pound of apples in a Soho market. "Why can't they leave us alone? Decimalization wasn't so bad but this mess is bloody stupid."

England is two years behind in its metrication program as a result of this recalcitrance by a stolid public—though British industry and British science have lent themselves to conversion with good will—and seems almost certain to lag further as time goes on. Beer and ale are now delivered to English pubs in metric containers but barmen have not demonstrated the slightest inclination to push them toward the customer in any measure but the hallowed English pint.

The Ford Motor Company—which has turned briskly toward conversion in England as in the United States—is now producing Britain's first all-metric automobile, the Cortina Mark III. Having done so, however, it is doing its best to hide this accomplishment from the buying public; it has carefully converted the machine's metric measurements back to old-fashioned standards, and distributes sales literature that describes the Cortina's weight in pounds, its gasoline capacity in gallons, and its interior carpeting in good old English square feet.

Any United States metric board that believes Americans will respond with more enthusiasm than is being demonstrated in the British Isles should leaf back in history and face up to sobering reality: The ordinary citizen has bridled at metrics in every country in the world upon which the system has been visited.

The French, themselves, have been doing so for 180 years. French peasants and tradesmen resisted metrics so stubbornly in the beginning that Napoleon, for all his dictatorial sense of mission, backed down and issued a decree permitting a resumption of medieval standards—including the "toise," which was six French feet, or *pieds du roi,* and originated as half the width of an inner gate at the Louvre. After the bureaucrats of Paris grew confident enough to outlaw the old standards forever in 1840, the citizenry substituted ancient terms for the high-sounding nomenclature of the metric system. Frenchmen buy their butter by the demi-kilo today—but ask the clerk for a *livre* for all that.

Still, the United States is not France or England. Adult Americans will doubtless embrace the new system as sullenly as their counterparts abroad, and will doubtless go on resenting it for years thereafter. But these millions of cranks will not live forever, and we must expect—since American youth is so revolted by tradition, so appalled by its parents' views, and is being so metricized, even now, in school systems—that the gram, the liter and the meter will be as American as marijuana in another 20 or 30 years. But metric nomenclature will certainly be Americanized—as have the sports, clothes, wine and, in fact, people we have imported from abroad. One would have to be rash, indeed, to wager that very much of the classical metric "language" will have survived, in unaltered form, in Dayton, Sacramento and the Bronx by the year 2000.

The European evidence supports this assumption. The French are not the only people to have given metrics a patina of plebeian synonym. A half liter is a *pinte* in Belgium and a half kilogram is a *pond* in Holland. There are practical as well as sentimental reasons for this stubborn and widespread practice of describing metric units by the names of their nearest old-fashioned equivalents, for this is a way of nondecimalizing the system, of making it possible to think of weights, quantities and measures in more familiar fractional terms, and of keying thought about them to the demands of everyday life.

"CLICKS," FOR A START

We are going to do the same thing, inevitably, ourselves. (If only because the meter is at such odds with United States housing—which nowadays is generally planned in terms of four-foot modules and built with eight-foot ceilings.)

But it is hard to think that a country so addicted to sardonic neologisms—and to change for the heady sake of change—will not do a more colorful job of it than the Europeans; and will not, in fact, re-do much more of the metric vocabulary than has been subject to mere regressive alteration abroad. It would be folly to try imagining the results of such a process now —though it may well have begun, and its tone may have been established, when GIs of World War II hit on the word "clicks" as a synonym for kilometers. But one thing about our approaching readjustment of habit and language does seem predictable. The United States will not undergo metric conversion without setting off an equal and opposite reaction as it does so. Metrics, too, will never be the same.

Centigrade or Fahrenheit, a hot day is still a scorcher in this vision of a not-too-distant future in which the metric system—with its meters, kilos, grams and Centigrade temperatures—has become as familiar to Americans as it long since has to most of the rest of the world's people.

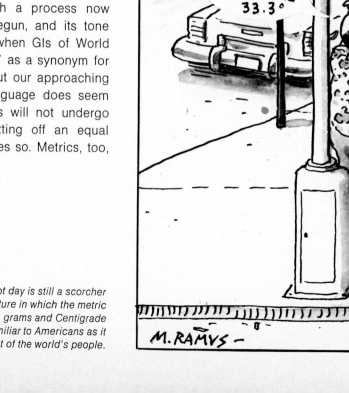

Finding Ways to Make the Deserts Bloom

At Kufra, in southeastern Libya, circular plots two thirds of a mile across speckle the barren Sahara sand with the green of sorghum, barley and—at right—wheat and alfalfa. In the Negev of Israel, where for more than a thousand years nothing has lived but scraggly desert weeds, there are now fields of peaches, almonds, onions and olives. From the island of Sadiyat, a blistering hot, almost rainless and soilless dot in the Persian Gulf, comes a steady supply of fresh vegetables for the sheikhdom of Abu Dhabi. Here and in many other arid parts of the world, once-useless land is being made productive with the aid of modern adaptations of old techniques.

None of these desert projects depends on dams and irrigation canals to bring water from distant sources. The Libyan farms make use of a newly tapped underground water supply—larger than Lake Superior. In Israel, archeologist-agronomists rebuilt ancient catchment systems to conserve scarce rainfall. The Abu Dhabians built greenhouses to grow a ton of vegetables a day in five acres of controlled environment.

Although each approach differs, all follow an increasingly recognized principle: make the best use of local conditions. For if the world's food sources are to be stretched to feed growing populations, both new ideas *(pages 140-141)* and old ones will be needed to make things grow under otherwise impossible conditions.

Circular fields of grain sprout from the Libyan desert at the edge of a gigantic irrigation project involving nearly 24,000 acres. The fields are circular because they get water from centrally rotated sprinklers; the water, from an underground reservoir, had fallen as rain perhaps 30,000 years ago.

One third of a mile in length, this irrigator, built in France, sprinkles a mixture of water and fertilizer over a field of barley.

Tapping the Sahara's Hidden Water

All the water flowing in the Nile for 200 years would barely equal the contents of the immense aquifer—an underground, water-soaked layer —uncovered under the Sahara in Libya in 1968. Located by geologists hunting oil, it is believed to cover 160,000 square miles, lying 10 feet to 2,500 feet beneath surface level, and to contain 200,000 billion gallons of water. The water ap- parently originated in rivers that, millennia ago, soaked into the ground in this area.

This ancient water is brought up—at the rate of 1,200 gallons a minute—by a diesel pump con- nected to an 1,850-foot sprinkler pipe riding on 14 carriages, each driven by its own electric mo- tor. The carriages drive the sprinklers along their circular courses.

Technicians connect an irrigation pipe to the wellhead at the center of a new field.

Wheat (left) does better than sorghum (far left) in the Libyan fields. The wheat, developed in Mexico, has strong stems that resist the desert's strong winds. It can yield as much as 6,000 pounds per acre yearly. The sorghum, a hybrid of Western and local species, has been less productive.

141

Maturing wheat, 24 inches high, flanks this narrow sandy track cut by the repeated passage of one of the 14 motorized carriages that wheel the overhead sprinkler around the field.

Bales of alfalfa hay, stacked 12 feet high, are used to feed the project's expanding herd of sheep. Farmers in Kufra hope to harvest as much as 15,000 tons of alfalfa per acre annually.

Barbary fat-tailed sheep feast on Kufra-grown hay. This indigenous species is well adapted to desert conditions: the large store of fat in its tail helps it live for days on a meager food supply.

In Israel, Biblical Farming Revived

One look at Israel's Negev Desert would convince anyone that the arid land can support nothing more than a few goats. Yet for a thousand years—until an Arab invasion in 641 A.D.—early farmers known as the Nabateans sustained a population of 150,000 there.

From the ruins of Nabatean homesteads *(below)*, Israeli scientists figured out the ancient methods. The Nabateans had taken advantage of sloping land and Negev soil, which forms a crust that soaks up rainfall very slowly. Infrequent rains—an average of three to four inches a year—were caught and directed by channels and low stone walls. These catchments slowed the runoff and brought it to lowland fields. There each plot was surrounded by more stone walls, to back up the water and to hold it until it had moistened the earth.

The ruins of Nabatean Avdat overlook a reconstructed farm in the valley and the runoff channels on the slopes above it.

A plump peach ripens in a Negev orchard, nourished by the skillful use of the scant rainfall. Traditional fruits of the semi-arid Near East—almonds, olives—do better, however.

Stone walls around farm plots back up the rainwater channeled from the hills, holding it to supply fruit trees and grasses.

This blooming mass of allium cepa—one of the winter crops at Avdat—is a new variety of onion well adapted to the desert

conditions of the Negev. It will be allowed to go to seed for use in future plantings and for sale to other desert farmers.

Artificial Environment on an Arabian Island

Sheikh Zayed, ruler of the 26,000 petroleum-soaked square miles of Abu Dhabi, on the Persian Gulf, reads neither English nor Arabic, but an aid told him about a 1967 article, in an American magazine, describing desert agriculture experiments by University of Arizona scientists. The project seemed tailored to the climate of Abu Dhabi—and the sheikh's treasury overflowed with petrodollars. A $3 million grant brought American scientists to develop such a project in Abu Dhabi.

The site of Abu Dhabi's farm is the small island of Sadiyat, one and a half miles off the mainland. It would take a genuine miracle to make anything grow naturally on Sadiyat. The temperature rises as high as 114°. The rainfall averages less than two inches per year, almost all in winter. The winds are strong, and bring salt spray from the gulf. Even the dirt is not really soil, but near-sterile sand. But cost was no hindrance, and the Arizona scientists set out to replace an impossible environment with a completely artificial one.

They erected greenhouses on five acres: 48 shallow structures, 22 feet by 90 feet, of plastic held up by compressed air for low-growing crops such as bush beans, cabbages and flowers; four tall, rigid ones, 42 feet by 204 feet, for tomatoes and cucumbers. The crops are irrigated with desalinated sea water (.2 cents a gallon, compared to around .003 cents for irrigation water in Arizona). The greenhouses help keep the plants warm in winter (in summer the greenhouses have to be cooled by sprays of sea water). But mainly they block winds and prevent moisture from evaporating too fast.

These five pampered acres yield an average of one ton of fresh vegetables daily—including cucumbers, which Abu Dhabians like so much they nibble on them as if they were candy bars.

Traditional ways meet the new as villagers walk their camels past Sadiyat Island's greenhouse compound. Only fishermen live on the island; the camels are pets that serve as status symbols. The island, a stretch of sterile sand, now produces 800,000 pounds of vegetables per year.

A local technician ties cucumber seedlings to support strings. Irrigation water containing fertilizer trickles from the black pipes alongside the seedlings growing in the desert sand.

Hamdy M. Eisa (with clipboard) and Merle H. Jensen of the University of Arizona's Environmental Research Laboratory, inspect a summer squash flower. They aim to select early-blooming types that will beat the summer heat, which inhibits the formation of female flowers, thereby reducing the amount of fruit borne.

Foot-long cucumbers are readied for ▶ the short boat ride to the wholesale market. Abu Dhabians, who were accustomed to cucumbers half that length, were reluctant to try this unfamiliar variety until they saw their ruler eat one on television.

Making Every Drop Count

The desert farmer's problem is not so much that he has no water as it is that he cannot get full value out of the water he has. Even in the Sahara there would be enough moisture to grow crops if every drop got inside the plants and stayed there to help them grow. But nature seems bent on wasting water, so that only a fraction of a per cent actually provides nourishment. These losses may now be halted as scientists develop techniques for plugging the leaks in the agricultural water system in order to help the world's deserts support crops with their own native resources.

There are at least four ways water disappears on its way to growing plant cells. It evaporates from the surface of farm ponds, irrigation channels and reservoirs; if their surface is large compared to the volume they contain, they may lose more water than they deliver for use. Then water evaporates from the surface of the soil; as much as half an irrigation supply may disappear in this way. And much of the half that does get into the soil sinks without a trace—in sandy desert soils the loss can be nearly total. The final frustration is the extravagance of the plants themselves: They throw away 99 per cent of the moisture they get, retaining in their cells only one per cent of the amount they absorb through their roots, and releasing the rest into the air through pores in their leaves. By this transpiration process, one acre of vegetation can waste as much as 10,000 gallons of water per day.

Until recently, only one of these leaks—surface evaporation—has been preventable. Farmers have long spread mulches around plants to keep wind and heat away from the ground and thus retard evaporation. Now more effective mulches of plastic, oil or rubber serve a dual purpose in deserts, where high winds shift the sands; the new substances prevent evaporation while holding the sand to let young plants root. One was used to hold down sand dunes in India's Rajasthan Desert, where some 60,000 young eucalyptus trees were planted; 90 per cent survived and doubled their height in their first year. Without the mulch, sand would have buried the saplings or blown away and exposed their roots.

To block evaporation from ponds and channels before water reaches a crop, several ingenious methods have been developed to seal off the surface and thus reduce the area where evaporation occurs, such as floating blocks of lightweight concrete, rubber or plastic on the pond, and the use of wax, which melts in the sun to form a continuous seal. The wax method, reports Keith R. Cooley of the United States Water Conservation Laboratory in Phoenix, Arizona, can prevent over 85 per cent of the loss.

More difficult to eliminate is leakage through the soil itself. In greenhouses like those at Abu Dhabi (pages 150-151), plant beds are lined with plastic sheets. But open fields are generally so big they demand mechanized systems. One new type of machine, used in Libya, drags a wedge-shaped plow 20 to 28 inches below the soil surface to throw up sand while a nozzle sprays asphalt in the plow's wake. The asphalt dries at once, forming a thin, water-blocking layer before the earth falls back into place. A different scheme, now being developed by William M. Doane of the U.S. Department of Agriculture at Peoria, Illinois, stops both seepage and surface evaporation by mixing the topsoil with chemicals capable of soaking up many times their weight in water; plants can then grow roots around the water-swollen clumps and get moisture from them. One mix that Doane calls a super slurper, made of starch and a plastic-like synthetic, can absorb 1,500 times its weight in water.

But the most profligate waste of water is caused by the plants, and many laboratories are testing compounds that can be sprayed on leaves to block transpiration through pores without interfering with growth. Among the most promising is a wax being tested at the University of California at Davis. It must be applied at the proper time—about two weeks before harvest—so that it conserves water and increases fruit size but does not prevent the intake of carbon dioxide for photosynthesis for growth.

Even if only a few of these conservation ideas pan out, the value to the world will be incalculable. Every drop of water saved will add to the productivity of the deserts, which form one of the last of the planet's still untapped sources of food.

A worker at Padre Island in Texas tests the consistency of sand sprayed with an oil-rubber mixture to help it retain moisture and to prevent erosion. The emulsion, developed in England, binds sand into a gummy mulch one fifth inch deep, forming a flexible membrane that blocks evaporation.

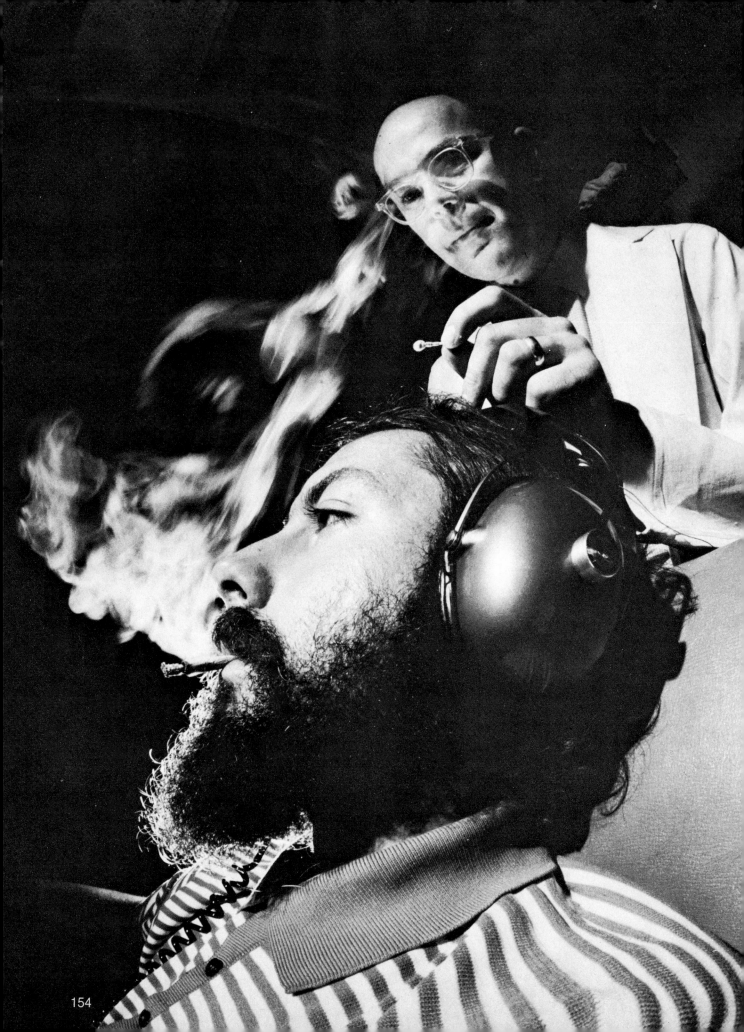

The Real Dope on Pot

NEW TESTS SUGGEST MARIJUANA MAY HAVE HARMFUL EFFECTS

by Arthur Fisher

J ust a few years ago there were some scientists going around saying, 'Isn't marijuana a wonderful drug? It produces psychological effects and nothing else.' There aren't many scientists saying that anymore." The speaker was Dr. Reese T. Jones of the University of California's Langley-Porter Neuropsychiatric Institute in San Francisco, one of the handful of United States medical researchers who have conducted rigidly controlled experiments into the effects of marijuana on human beings. His comment, made early in 1975, points to an ironic turn in the strange and tangled history of marijuana use: Just as the legal establishment is moving to eliminate criminal penalties for use and possession, the medical establishment is turning up evidence—though much is preliminary and some disputed—that marijuana, in regular, heavy doses, may after all be harmful.

The evidence, most of it published in *Marihuana and Health,* a government report of November 1974, is based on meticulous research. It raises questions about earlier investigations, such as the widely publicized study of marijuana smokers in Jamaica, which found the drug innocuous, but the new findings are controversial. Some of the tests involved artificially heavy doses. Also, some "bad" effects may prove to be helpful: One piece of government research hints marijuana might inhibit some cancers.

Moreover, researchers are well aware of marijuana's powerful—and still justified—reputation for safety, based largely on the drug's long-established and extensive use. Made from the

In one of the first medical experiments using accurate and controlled doses of marijuana, a volunteer subject smokes a standardized joint while a research scientist of the University of California, San Francisco, adjusts electrodes monitoring the brain's response to sound. The result: a depressant effect on brain functions similar to that produced by alcohol. Subsequent tests demonstrated even more serious damage to both mind and body.

Indian hemp plant, *Cannabis sativa,* marijuana has been known as a psychoactive drug for some 3,000 years and by 500 B.C. was apparently widely used in Central Asia, India and China. Today it grows freely in many parts of the world and has provided a psychedelic experience for hundreds of millions of people; it ranks, along with alcohol, caffeine and tobacco, as one of the most widely used drugs in the world.

RAPID RISE IN MARIJUANA USE

In the United States, consumption has increased steadily over the last few years. In October 1974, the Drug Abuse Council estimated, from a nationwide survey of marijuana use in a representative cross-section of adults and teenagers, that 29 million Americans have tried marijuana at least once, and over 12 million use it regularly. Another 1974 survey, of 23-year-old men, conducted by the Institute for Social Research at the University of Michigan, showed that in this age group 14 per cent smoked marijuana daily. Only 10 per cent used alcohol daily.

Until recently, the drug's sweeping popularity in America involved a sharp, ill-informed conflict between the pro- and antimarijuana forces. The tough laws against pot smoking—the result of uncompromising efforts over 30 years by law-enforcement officials to brand the drug a killer —were widely ignored as leading intellectuals proclaimed pot essentially innocuous.

Neither side, however, had any firm medical evidence for its opinions, for three separate reasons. Until the late 1960s, the federal government actively discouraged experimentation with marijuana on humans. Any legal experiment needed both legally acquired marijuana and official sanction, and federal agencies set up such a thicket of bureaucratic red tape that attempts to experiment with marijuana could not penetrate it.

Second, the available sources of marijuana varied so widely in quality and strength that it was practically impossible for scientists to measure and compare results accurately. The potency of marijuana depends on where the plant is grown, whether it is wild or cultivated, what part is used and how the preparation is made.

The most potent form of cannabis is the pure resin taken from carefully cultivated plants. This is available as cakes called charas in India and hashish in the Middle East. At the bottom of the scale is the crude combination of leaves, and sometimes stems, of the wild plant. This is the marijuana, pot, weed, grass—it has many other popular names as well—that is commonly smoked in hand-rolled joints, sprinkled over salads or baked into brownies or cookies.

The third element that made research impossible was the fact that no one knew the active constituents in the psychoactive resin, or just why it produced the effect it did. Therefore, it was not possible to standardize the purity and quality of the constituent chemicals in a manner that—as in any scientific experiment—allows the work to be performed, recorded, repeated and compared meaningfully.

The combination of government opposition, variable preparations and ignorance baffled researchers until 1967, when two events freed them from their shackles. First, the National Institute of Mental Health established the Center for the Study of Narcotics and Drug Abuse, now supplanted by the National Institute on Drug Abuse (NIDA). This bureaucratic reshuffling marked a turning point in official attitudes toward drug research. Then, in the same year, an Israeli chemist, Raphael Mechoulam, working at Jerusalem's Hebrew University, managed to synthesize a substance he had previously isolated from hemp plants, a chemical identified as delta-9-tetrahydrocannabinol, or THC for short. THC is now generally accepted to be the chief, though not the only, active agent in marijuana, and, with the announcement of Mechoulam's discovery, scientists could prepare the standardized doses essential to controlled experimental work.

Research could now begin in earnest. In 1968, as part of the new governmental policy, NIDA underwrote a five-acre marijuana farm at the University of Mississippi at Oxford, operated by its School of Pharmacy. The pot plantation, as it is irreverently called, furnishes marijuana to make a standard "NIDA joint," which contains roughly 1.8 per cent to 2.3 per cent THC. (By contrast, high-grade hashish has about 10 per cent THC.) Scientists could now freely conduct and control experiments using either the standard joints or measured doses of THC.

One of the first major findings, made soon after Mechoulam's discovery, was that THC is potentially far more dangerous than other common drugs because it takes considerably longer to work its way through the body; it does not mix with water, and therefore does not wash out of the body rapidly, as caffeine and alcohol do. Instead it mixes with fat, and this characteristic makes it persistent; like DDT, it remains for many days in any part of the body where there are fat deposits. Some of these areas are highly vulnerable to chemical action: the brain, the sheaths of major nerve fibers, the adrenal glands that secrete hormones to regulate a variety of bodily reactions, the sex organs—ovaries or testes.

As the pace of work accelerated in the United States, the effect of marijuana on these areas and the consequences in behavior have come under close scrutiny in a dozen different programs. They have turned up worrisome evidence that marijuana in sufficiently high doses may be harmful in seven areas, which range from very specific reactions on the body chemistry of men, through increasingly more general effects on the bodies of both men and women, and finally on mental attitudes and behavior. The effects are:

• reduction of the most important male hormone, or chemical agent, that controls sex
• reduction in the growth-control hormone
• impairment of the immune response system, which causes the body to reject foreign substances, not only disease-causing viruses and bacteria, but also skin grafts and some cancers
• damage to the lungs similar to that caused by cigarette smoking
• creation of physical dependence, so that a heavy marijuana user who quits will suffer withdrawal symptoms
• erosion of the will and desire to concentrate over extended periods
• lessened alertness, coordination, judgment and dexterity, which interfere with complex activities—notably driving

Perhaps the most important study so far is one concerning the effects of marijuana on the concentration of a male sex hormone in the blood.

At the Reproductive Biology Research Foundation in St. Louis, a team headed by Dr. Robert Kolodny (and including the foundation's director, Dr. William H. Masters, who, with his wife, Virginia Johnson, is probably the world's best-known expert on sexual behavior) picked 20 healthy young men 18 to 28 years old with a history of fairly heavy marijuana use.

The men had averaged three and a half years of regular smoking, but none reported using other drugs, except for alcohol in moderation. The men were matched in everything save marijuana use with a control group of 20. When both groups were given blood tests to gauge the levels of various sex hormones, the results were astounding. Testosterone, a regulator of sexual activity, averaged 44 per cent lower in the marijuana users than in the control group.

The hormone levels seemed to be related to the amount of marijuana smoked: Men using 10 or more joints a week had significantly less testosterone than men smoking fewer than 10 a week. Moreover, six of the smokers had lowered sperm counts and two of the men were impotent. When three of the subjects went off marijuana for two weeks, their testosterone levels bounced back again. When one of the impotent men stopped smoking marijuana, his problem, after a while, cleared up (the other declined to give up the drug, apparently preferring pot to potency).

Kolodny was the first to caution that this study was not definitive. The researchers' sample was small, they had only their subjects' word that other drugs had not been used, and they had no way of knowing the purity or strength of the marijuana used in the past. Nor were they sure whether all the men had normal sperm and testosterone levels before smoking marijuana.

The implications of the study, however, were important enough to raise serious questions. For instance, what were the drug's effects on babies born to women who used marijuana heavily in early pregnancy? ''We know,'' Kolodny stated, ''that some of the active ingredients of marijuana can spread from the bloodstream of the mother into the blood of her unborn baby. We also know that the normal development of the male—including the development of the sex or-

Marijuana, Cannabis sativa, is a plant with separate male (above) and female (far right) forms. The male, about three feet high, resembles giant ragweed, with a thin stem and short alternating branches usually bearing three- to five-lobed spiky leaves and clusters of flowers (inset). The aromatic resin that contains the intoxicant THC is present in all parts of the plant; but the top leaves and the flowers produce THC at concentrations up to 7 per cent.

Lush female marijuana plants sway in this well-tended ''pot plantation''—America's only legal marijuana farm—at the University of Mississippi, where the School of Pharmacy grows cannabis for use in many research laboratories.

The female marijuana plant closely resembles the male, but often towers up to 30 feet—10 times the height of the male—and produces marijuana in considerably higher concentrations. This fact undoubtedly was the basis of the ancient and widespread myth—that has only lately been disproved—that the male is totally lacking in potency. Resin from the two hard, bristly pods that contain the seed (inset) holds up to 11 per cent of the active chemical, THC.

gans—depends on the right amounts of testosterone being present at the right times. These crucial times occur at approximately the third and the fourth months of pregnancy. If testosterone levels in the baby are depressed because the mother is using marijuana, then his sexual development might be permanently impaired."

The lack of testosterone at these critical times has not yet been shown to have a direct effect on babies, but other studies in a quite different context suggest the effects might conceivably be disastrous. Testosterone deficiency can cause a baby who should be a boy to be born with underdeveloped or missing male sex organs, making him physically and emotionally more like a girl than a boy. This error cannot be completely corrected. The baby cannot be made into a normal male, but can be given a girl's body with surgery and later hormone treatments. She will then be a normal woman in every outward re-spect; however, she can never bear children.

Kolodny's test findings—which raise concern about other stages of life, such as puberty, when hormone levels are crucial to normal development—have been both contradicted and confirmed by other researchers. One scientist, Dr. Jack Mendelson of Harvard Medical School, tested marijuana smokers over a three-week period and failed to turn up any evidence of testosterone lowering. But two other studies by Dr. Sidney Cohen of the Neuropsychiatric Institute at UCLA and Dr. Reese T. Jones of the Langley-Porter Neuropsychiatric Institute in San Francisco did provide some evidence of testosterone reduction. In addition, Dr. Jones found indications of an effect on growth hormone.

Human growth hormone, manufactured lavishly in teenage boys, helps regulate development of bone and muscle, and is partly responsible for the often spectacular sprouting seen in adoles-

The view of marijuana smoking as sinful—regardless of its real effects—was established in the United States by 1876, when the Illustrated Police News depicted a probably imaginary "hasheesh hell on Fifth Avenue."

SECRET DISSIPATION OF NEW YORK BELLES—INTERIOR OF A HASHEESH HELL ON FIFTH AVENUE, WHILE IN FULL BLAST

cence, when a boy who is a dumpy five feet five inches one year may stretch into a lanky five-foot-nine-inch basketball center the next. "If growth hormone really is being diminished at this critical time," says Kolodny, "it's conceivable that the growth rate could be slowed or even that ultimate growth might be stunted."

Such research has suggested thus far only that marijuana influences hormone concentrations in the blood. What further effect—if any—may be involved remains to be determined. There is, as yet, no evidence that marijuana-induced hormone changes do in fact generate abnormal sexual and growth patterns. But, if such changes turn up, one other piece of research—into the age of marijuana smokers—has alarming implications. According to the longest-running survey of marijuana smoking—conducted by Lillian Blackford in San Mateo County, California—the greatest increase in smoking occurs between the ages of 12 and 14, the most vulnerable period of sexual development in male teenagers.

The studies on sex and growth hormones have measured marijuana's effects only on males; but there is evidence of another, more wide-ranging effect that involves the sexes equally. The drug may tamper with the human cell in a way that could result in the impairment of the body's ability to combat disease. This ability, called the immune response, involves an enormously complex set of defenses against invaders—viruses and other disease organisms, as well as proteins that are foreign to the body, some kinds of cancer, organ transplants and skin grafts.

One member of the corps of defenders against such foreign invasions is the white blood cell known as the T-lymphocyte. The T-lymphocytes are in a sense general shock troops. Whenever a virus or other foreign invader appears, the T-lymphocytes multiply at enormous rates, swarm to the front lines and destroy the enemy.

In 1973 , Dr. Gabriel G. Nahas and his colleagues at Columbia University's College of Physicians and Surgeons isolated T-lymphocytes from the blood of regular marijuana users and "challenged" them—tested how they would fight two different invaders, either of which would ordinarily have stimulated the T-lymphocytes to

heroic feats of multiplication in an attempt to overwhelm them. Nahas found that the efficiency of T-lymphocytes in marijuana users was about 40 per cent below normal. He concluded that the immune response of some marijuana smokers might be seriously compromised, leaving them more vulnerable than nonmarijuana smokers to a variety of diseases. As he acknowledged, however, this test-tube result could not be documented by evidence that pot users actually suffered a greater incidence of disease.

Nahas' conclusions are hotly disputed; an attempt to duplicate his results in early 1975 failed, and another experiment seemed to contradict it. But in two research units, Nahas' findings have been partially confirmed. One of these is the Neuropsychiatric Institute at UCLA, where Dr. Sidney Cohen affirmed that "we are finding at least preliminary agreement with Nahas on T-lymphocytes." Further confirmation of some aspects of Nahas' work comes from Dr. Louis Harris, Professor of Pharmacology at the Medical College of Virginia in Richmond.

"We became interested in Dr. Nahas' research," says Harris, "because we're pioneers in organ transplants, which are so often rejected as foreign by the body's immune response system. We wanted to learn if marijuana, or THC, had any effect on the role of T-lymphocytes in rejecting organ transplants. We found that when you give THC to mice with skin grafts—say black skin on a white mouse—the mouse's ability to reject the graft is impaired, indicating some lowering of immune-response effectiveness."

LUNG DAMAGE TOO?

The interference with hormones and the immune system is not the only harm blamed on marijuana. The THC that produces these effects is only one of several potentially dangerous constituents in marijuana smoke. Another is a more ordinary group of chemicals, known as tar. Smoke from a joint might therefore do as much lung damage as tar-rich tobacco smoke. This possibility was first raised in the 1960s, when lung disorders were found to be common among GI's who were heavy hashish smokers in Germany.

Now Dr. Jack Mendelson, reporting on his hospital studies of marijuana smokers, says: "Our findings suggest that people who smoke marijuana may get into lung trouble. . . . We think we've ruled out an origin in tobacco smoking, because we found it in men who don't smoke tobacco cigarettes at all—just pot. This was the pattern in about 25 per cent of our subjects. The tar concentration in marijuana cigarettes is much higher than in tobacco cigarettes, and of course pot smokers hold the smoke in their lungs for much longer periods than tobacco smokers. So there may be a decided association between lung damage and marijuana and it may have nothing to do with the THC content."

That speculation is supported, in part, by a recent experiment conducted by Harvard's Dr. Gary L. Huber at Beth Israel Hospital in Boston. He extracted macrophages—cells that devour foreign bacteria—from the lungs of rats, then mixed them with a common bacterial invader. In three hours, the macrophages destroyed about three quarters of the bacterial population. Then Huber repeated the test while exposing the test-tube mixture to tobacco smoke, marijuana smoke and smoke from marijuana cigarettes from which all THC had been removed. He found that smoke from all three sources prevented the macrophages from responding in roughly the same proportion. Filtering the solid particles out of marijuana smoke did not change the effect at all. But when Huber filtered the smoke through water, the resulting product did not inhibit the macrophages in the least.

A POSSIBLE CAUSE OF CANCER

One implication of this research is that marijuana smoke could turn out to be a cause of cancer, as tobacco smoke is. So far, almost nothing has been done to establish whether there is any connection between lung cancer and marijuana smoking. However, a Swiss team, Drs. Cecile and Rudolph Leuchtenberger, have found that human lung tissue cultured outside the body shows cell abnormalities when exposed to both tobacco and marijuana smoke. Whether this reflects what actually happens in the lungs is unknown.

All these physical risks would be much more serious if marijuana turned out to be a physically addictive drug like alcohol or barbiturates. Now there are indications that heavy doses could create tolerance to marijuana. Increasingly high doses would then be required to get the same effect. Eventually, a certain intake level would become essential to the body chemistry, and the user would become physically dependent on it.

For years, writers on marijuana insisted that the body did not develop tolerance to the drug. In fact, it was part of pot folklore that users enjoyed a reverse tolerance—with experience, a smoker needed less of the drug to get the same high. Like several other myths about marijuana, that one seems to have gone up in smoke during the last two years. In the experiment conducted at the Langley-Porter Neuropsychiatric Institute in San Francisco, Reese Jones states flatly, "We have produced clear-cut tolerance. We give our volunteer research subjects, who are all experienced marijuana users, THC orally, every four hours around the clock. The very large dose we give them is probably the equivalent to the amount of THC in about 10 to 20 NIDA joints.

"We expected people to be stoned constantly when given these very high doses. But that's not what happens. Tolerance begins within a few days. After awhile, you might as well be giving them sugar pills. After two weeks on this dose some of the subjects don't even believe we're giving them the drug anymore. I used to be skeptical of the reports from some of our research subjects claiming they smoke the equivalent of 20 to 30 joints a day—now I am less so.

"Moreover, we see a pattern of symptoms after sudden withdrawal of the THC that could well result from the development of mild dependence—it resembles the withdrawal syndrome from alcohol and barbiturates. Our research subjects have experienced insomnia, restlessness, irritability, loss of appetite, sweating, weight loss when they go off the THC—and sometimes tremor, loose bowel movements and vomiting."

Apart from the immediate physical and chemical effects, the wide-ranging influence of marijuana on the body raises another disturbing question: Since it affects the whole body and since it is known to linger in the brain, might not prolonged smoking lead to changes in attitude and behavior far more serious than the transitory high sought by the user? The question is a natural one because for years researchers have speculated about an amotivational syndrome —jargon for a cumulative "turn on, tune in, drop out" effect that supposedly robs some heavy users of the motivation to work. There is now some preliminary, limited evidence from tests made by Jack Mendelson.

In one of these work tests at Boston City Hospital, 20 volunteers, half of whom had been heavy and half casual users of marijuana, lived in a hospital ward for 31 days. The men earned money, which they could either keep or use to buy and smoke marijuana joints (at the rate of 50 cents a joint) during the middle three weeks of the study. They earned the points by pushing a button on a portable device much like a TV remote control. All the subjects earned the maximum points allowed—$10 worth a day—by pushing the buttons about once a second for six to eight hours a day —as many as 27,000 pushes.

Dr. Mendelson summarized the results: "We were asking the question 'Do people turn off work with marijuana?' We found that on the contrary, even smoking up to 18 or 19 joints a day, nothing happened. The men earned their maximum every day; there was no fall-off in output at all. This was remarkable when compared to the same kind of experiment with alcohol addicts. When these men got their alcohol, their work output fell to zilch."

This first study was widely cited (but not by Mendelson) as offering proof that there was *no* amotivational syndrome due to marijuana use. Then Mendelson performed essentially the same experiment again, this time with 28 volunteers at McLean Hospital in Belmont, Massachusetts, and with a more generous pay scale. "We could afford to remove the limit on the amount of points and dollars that could be earned. Now we found an even greater rate of work output at first, 10 to 11 hours of 3,600-times-an-hour button pushing. But on the last five days, we saw something new: a very significant fall-off in work output." In these five days, for both heavy and casual users, the number of joints smoked one day was followed the next day by a decrease in points earned.

At first, this seems understandable enough; anyone doing such a boring task could hardly be expected to keep up such a high performance. But in fact simple boredom can apparently be ruled out. In one of Mendelson's other studies, subjects working for money without drugs kept on pushing their buttons at the same high rate until the end of the experiment. Comments Mendelson, "There is *something* in these results. Suppose we doubled or tripled the dose; then I think we'd produce some real derangements in motivation, perhaps the kind associated with alcoholism and barbiturate addiction."

Besides examining the question of an amotivational syndrome, scientists have looked into another widely held belief about the effects of marijuana on behavior: that the drug did not influence the ability to drive, or at least did so less than alcohol. In 1972, Dr. Harry Klonoff, Professor of Psychiatry at the University of British Columbia in Vancouver, began a two-year study that proved the belief was without foundation. He tested 64 experienced men and women drivers —young, well educated and all previous pot smokers—to see how marijuana affected their actual performance behind the wheel of a car. And the tests were conducted not just on a restricted, traffic-free course, but also in the hectic traffic of downtown Vancouver (in cars equipped with dual controls). Obtaining the necessary permissions and insurance for this test was probably the hardest part of the study.

The volunteers first went through a driving course fiendishly equipped with a slalom, tunnels (narrow lanes between traffic cones) and various complex backing and turning maneuvers. After several practice runs, they were scored on driving performance by a trained observer. Then they repeated the test after smoking a marijuana cigarette. Subsequently, 38 of the subjects drove through downtown Vancouver's busy streets.

Results: Smoking a single joint impaired the driving performance of most of the subjects. On the closed course, some drivers forgot which task they had to do next, drove off the course, or neglected to shift into reverse when backing up. Performance in the real-life situation of actual traffic also markedly deteriorated, and here the potential for accidents appeared dramatically. Drivers ran traffic lights and stop signs, passed recklessly and often seemed confused or dangerously unaware of the movements of pedestrians and other vehicles.

Klonoff's conclusion: "It is evident that the smoking of marijuana by human subjects does have a detrimental effect on their driving skills and performance in a restricted driving area, and that this effect is even greater under normal conditions of driving on city streets. . . . Driving under the influence of marijuana should be avoided as much as driving under the influence of alcohol."

BENEFITS BOTH OLD AND NEW

Although much of the new marijuana research has turned up potentially harmful effects, there is also evidence that marijuana has several of those beneficial effects that have always been claimed for it, and some more besides. In many parts of the world, it has long been used in folk medicine for relieving pain and for sedation, effects confirmed by current research. Two studies in 1974 showed that the threshold of pain, as determined by the electrical stimulation to the skin, decreased when the subjects were dosed with marijuana. In other studies, the drug helped insomniacs get to sleep quicker (though some were left with a hangover or awoke still high) and reduced the time for anesthetics to take effect. In mild doses, it has also been shown to be a tranquilizer and a relaxant, easing the breathing of bronchial and asthmatic patients.

One effect could find specific clinical application in the treatment of glaucoma, a disease of the eye caused by an increase of fluid in the eyeball. In experiments with rabbits reported by K. Green and J. E. Pederson, the injection of THC caused a decrease in fluid pressure but similar tests have not yet been done on human beings.

Even broader hope for the medical use of marijuana is suggested by Dr. Louis Harris' work on the drug's effect on the immune response. If THC can inhibit a mouse's immune response and prevent it from rejecting skin grafts, it possibly could do the same thing for humans, thus helping surgeons to overcome the problems of rejection of grafts and transplants. The second benefit concerns THC's effect on cancer. Harris reasoned, with apparently indisputable logic, that since the immune response fights cancer, and marijuana inhibits the immune response, marijuana should make the body more vulnerable to cancer. He decided to test this hypothesis by giving THC to mice implanted with solid tumors.

"The results were just the opposite of what we expected," he reports. "The growth of the tumors was slowed, and the mice lived 35 to 40 per cent longer than mice with the same kinds of tumor implants who were *not* given THC. The chemical compound from marijuana was effective against at least three kinds of solid tumor." But why did the tumors grow more slowly, not faster? The answer, Harris thinks, is that THC impairs the rate of chemical change—and thus the growth—of the cancer cells even more than that of the immune system's T-lymphocytes.

"But all this is speculative, and we're still very puzzled," Dr. Harris continues. "We're nowhere near a possible cure for cancer. What we do have, however, is a class of chemical agents that interfere with tumor growth in a different way from other chemical agents. And there will definitely be experiments in which human subjects with cancer will be treated with marijuana or its active agents."

Harris' work is a powerful reminder of how little is known as yet about the effects of marijuana. But progress has been rapid, and rigorous, and much of what has already been learned gives cause for concern. Dr. Robert L. DuPont, NIDA's director, sums it up this way: "Although it is still impossible to put numbers on the relative degrees of risk from marijuana use, there is clearer scientific evidence of health hazards than we had in the past. If a person is thinking about using marijuana, he's better off not using it. If he's using it, he ought to use it as little as possible.

"For a grownup who is well-integrated, and realizes he's going to be intoxicated after marijuana and therefore doesn't make any demands on himself—like driving—and who doesn't escalate the dose, a couple of joints a month *probably* won't do any damage. But the evidence should make people question whether marijuana is really worth the risk."

Magnified 1,200 times, nodules of resin—from which hashish, the most potent form of marijuana, is made—ooze from the glandular hairs of a female cannabis plant.

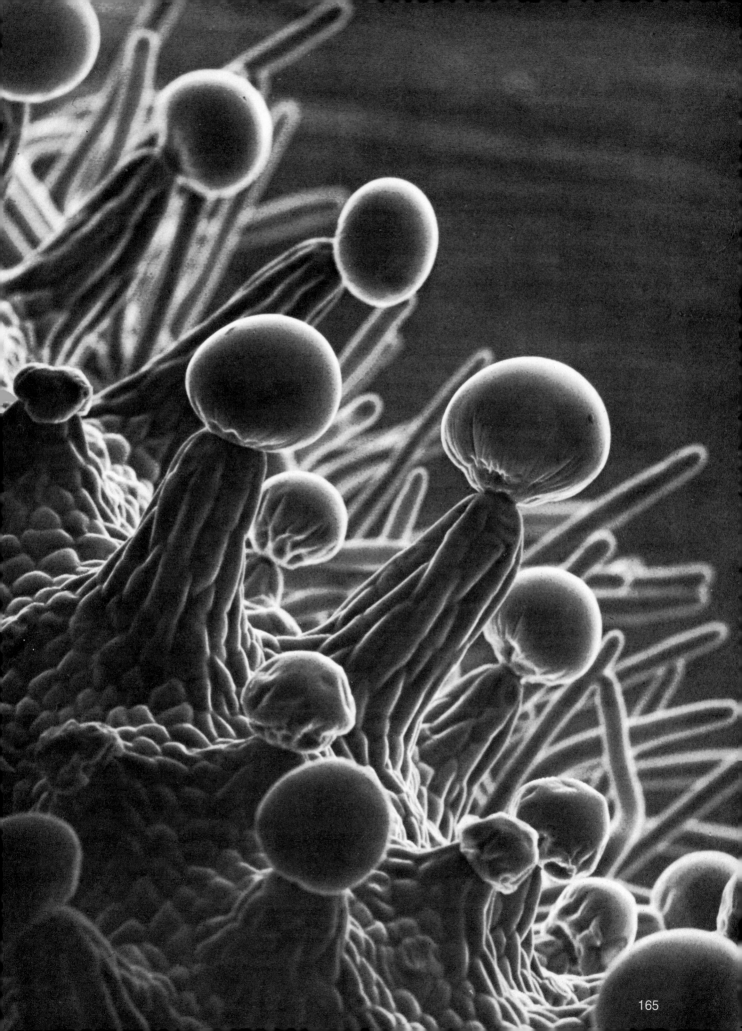

The Flying Giant of Texas

Big Bend National Park, on the border of Texas and Mexico, is mostly a harsh desert of canyons and mesas, relieved only by a skimpy cover of scrub and coarse grass. But 65 million years ago, toward the end of the age of dinosaurs, it was a very different place. Then, in the late Cretaceous period, swampy lowlands, rank with ferns, cattails and water-loving trees, combined with a stable subtropical climate to provide ideal conditions for the region's many reptilian species—among them, the largest airborne creature in the history of the world.

The gigantic flying reptile was reported in March 1975, by a young University of Texas paleontologist, Douglas Lawson, who had discovered the first—and most imposing—of the bones in 1971. Knowing that the park's ancient sediments could be rich in fossils, he had painstakingly crisscrossed the area on a number of different visits. One day he spotted some bone partially exposed on the face of a low hill. A little excavation revealed bits of a wing. By 1974, with the help of later finds, Lawson had identified these as fragments of a gigantic, previously unknown species of pterosaur, a general term for all the airborne reptiles that thrived between 65 million and 150 million years ago.

Many species of pterosaur had long been known. Some were only a few inches long; one, *Pteranodon ingens,* had wings that extended 25 feet, twice the span of the wandering albatross, the largest flying animal in existence today. The Big Bend finds suggested a creature still bigger. From a 17½-inch humerus—the wing bone that pivots on the shoulder—Lawson calculated that the animal had a wingspan of around 50 feet, twice the size of the pteranodon.

Lawson's report of the huge pterosaur set off a flurry of debate and speculation. Many experts had considered the pteranodon little more than an exceptionally skillful glider that could hardly flap at all. No one could imagine how an animal twice as large and much heavier could take off and gain altitude. Yet Lawson's analysis of his fossils and a newly published re-examination of the pteranodon suggest that the huge Texas pterosaur—as it was immediately dubbed—could indeed fly like a bird.

There has never been much question about the flying abilities of small pterosaurs. But size brings problems: As size increases, weight goes up even faster. A larger body needs broader wings, which demand increasingly large back-up systems of muscle, bone, heart, lungs and digestive tract. The effects are dramatic: When size is doubled—assuming shape and structure remain in proportion—weight increases eightfold. Other factors, like strain on the wings and power requirements, increase in proportions that are similarly imposing.

It was formerly believed that the upper limit for airborne size had been reached by the pteranodon. Despite its 25-foot span it weighed a scant 35 pounds. Only 30 per cent of it was solid; the rest was taken up with air sacs. Its wing bones had walls of eggshell delicacy—only one twenty-fifth inch or so thick—and its wing membranes as well were paper thin. Even so, the pteranodon seemed too heavy to rely much on the flapping flight that is common to most birds. According to a 1974 study by two English scientists, Cherrie Bramwell and George Whitfield of Reading University, the pteranodon, with its presumably birdlike musculature, required so much muscle to flap that it could generate only just enough lift to take off from level ground and

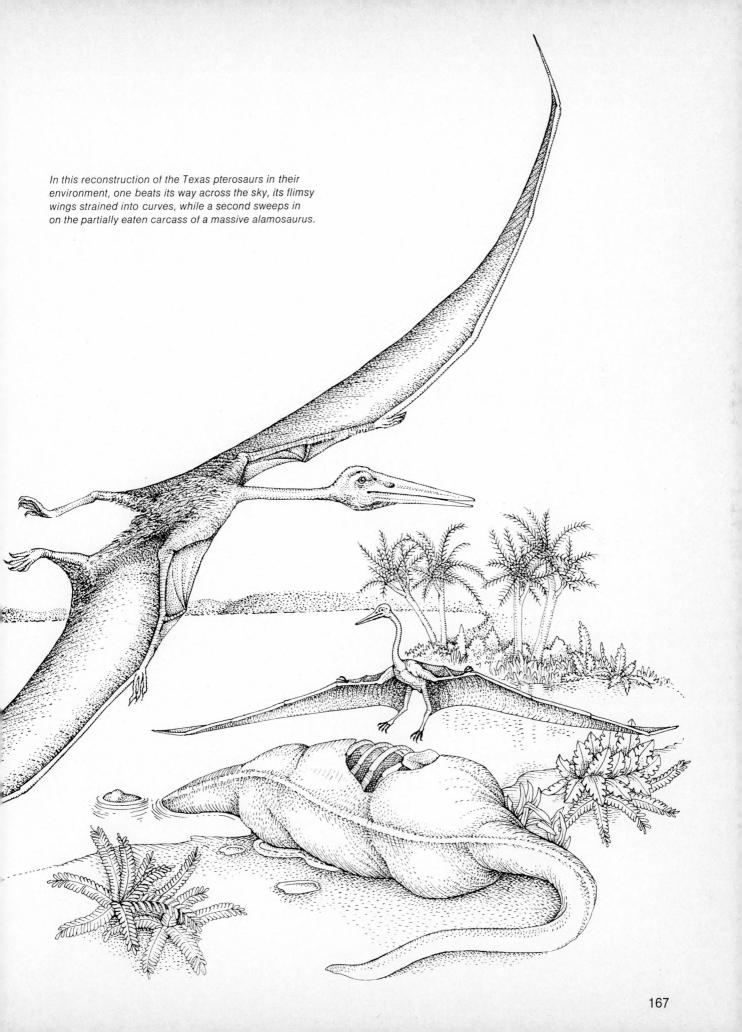

In this reconstruction of the Texas pterosaurs in their environment, one beats its way across the sky, its flimsy wings strained into curves, while a second sweeps in on the partially eaten carcass of a massive alamosaurus.

could hardly climb at all under its own power.

The pteranodon provided apparently clear guidelines to the size and habits of all large pterosaurs. Anything of similar build, apparently, could not get much bigger without upsetting the critical balance of wingspan, weight and muscle. Moreover, it would have to live on coastal cliffs, since to avoid the continual strains of takeoff it would have to feed on the wing and would probably be a fisheater.

The Texas pterosaur broke all these rules.

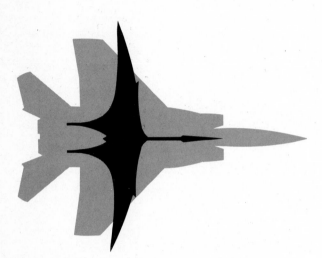

The pterosaur outspanned a modern fighter plane—above, it is sketched over the 42-foot McDonnell Douglas 5-15 A.

First, there was no doubting its size. Second, the bones were found 200 miles away from any Cretaceous seas. And third, it must have landed to feed—and taken off again afterward—for its neck vertebrae did not allow for the up-and-down motion necessary for fishing on the wing.

If the Texas pterosaur was a scaled-up version of the pteranodon, it would have weighed 290 pounds, too solid ever to have gotten off the ground. But the fossil wing bone strongly suggests flight, for it has a huge bulge at one end, almost certainly a support for powerful wing muscles. And, although hollow, it is strengthened internally by minutely corrugated slats of bone to resist the lengthwise compression applied by muscles on takeoff.

In May, a study of pteranodon flight by Ross Stein, a geologist at Brown University, indicated that the pteranodon flew better than had been thought. If it did, then the Texas pterosaur might have flown similarly. Stein tested scale-model pteranodon wings in a wind tunnel and found they acted like a yacht's sail laid horizontally, bellying up behind the "mast" of the wing bone. Unlike a mast, however, the pteranodon's wing bones could rotate to alter the angle of the wing's leading edges, a vital requirement for flapping flight. Also, the wing was quite flexible, allowing it to whiplash and impart a powerful, uplifting flick to the tip. Finally, Stein said, the pteranodon could well have generated more than enough power to flap if its muscles were like those of a bat, which account for no more than 10 per cent of its weight, rather than those of a bird, which make up as much as 35 per cent of body weight.

On the basis of these conclusions, it is possible to sketch a speculative portrait of the Texas pterosaur. It would have been able to glide well, but it could also have flapped efficiently, allowing it to take off and land with the delicacy demanded by its spindly structure. Its huge wings would have had tremendous flexibility and the whiplash effect identified by Stein would have been exaggerated into flowing wavelike beats —vital if the creature was to avoid hitting the ground with its wing tips on takeoff.

With such devices—and perhaps others that are yet to be discovered—the Texas pterosaur, though still proportionately much weaker than the pteranodon, would at least have been able to get off the ground. And that, given the hot, stable Cretaceous climate, would be enough. A few languorous flaps would take the creature into the rising columns of hot air, or thermals, that begin at heights of from 50 to 100 feet over land and enable gliders, both natural and man-made, to stay aloft for hours.

Once up, it would have been able to soar over the plains for around 200 miles daily with scarcely a wingbeat. This range would have suited its presumed life style, for the big Texas pterosaur's neck bones suggest it was a scavenger. The fossil vertebrae are exceptionally long: The best preserved ones, which are from *smaller* individuals, are up to 16 inches long. Since there were seven vertebrae in a pterosaur's neck, even a

At Big Bend, Douglas Lawson holds the wing bone that is evidence both of the pterosaur's size and ability to fly. The bulge where flight muscles were presumably attached is clearly visible.

conservative estimate would give the creature a reach of eight or nine feet, including head and beak. On this basis, Lawson, who is now refining his theories at the University of California at Berkeley, concluded that the Texas pterosaur could have been a carrion eater that used its sinuous neck to probe the carcasses of the tremendous herbivorous dinosaurs that browsed the marshy vegetation.

This picture, though based largely on circumstantial evidence, is further supported by one suggested explanation of the extinction of the pterosaurs. Such huge fliers would have been extremely susceptible to high winds, which would simply crumple them up in the air. The English expert George Whitfield estimates that an increase in average wind speed of only 10 miles per hour would make life impossible for the pteranodon, let alone the more vulnerable Texas pterosaur. At the end of the Cretaceous period, when the dinosaurs and most other ancient forms of reptilian life abruptly and mysteriously died out, the wind did change. The world grew colder, temperature differences increased, winds grew stronger, and the Texas pterosaur was swept from the skies.

JOHN MAN

Summing Up the Year

A BRIEF REVIEW OF EVENTS, DISCOVERIES AND DEVELOPMENTS

ANIMAL BEHAVIOR

The subtleties of animal perception and communication continued to make news. Apes and monkeys recognize their own kind as readily as humans, and they "talk" to one another in complex body language; army ants rely on scout "reports" to find food, and a cannibal firefly mimics the flashing pattern of its prey as a lure. Finally, scientists explained why insects may need plants to reproduce and how tuna fish maintain a higher body temperature than other fish.

BIGOTED MONKEYS

Like biased people who think persons of a different race all look the same, monkeys fail to recognize distinctions in other animals. Cambridge psychologist Nick K. Humphrey reported that young rhesus monkeys trained to press buttons to view pictures on a screen spent much more time viewing rhesus monkeys than they spent watching unfamiliar animals like pigs and goats. Humphrey concluded that although the monkeys saw their fellow kin as individuals, they tended to lump the "foreigners" together, making no distinction between species or between individuals of the same species. To them monkeys were fascinating, but a pig was just a pig.

When the same monkeys looked at slides of cats and dogs and then were tested, Humphrey found they had become sophisticated. Able to make fine distinctions between animals, they now "treated individual cats and dogs as being as different from one another as individual monkeys."

LANGUAGE OF THE CHIMPS

ACTING ON COMMUNICATIONS FROM ITS FELLOWS, A CHIMP PROBES FOR A SNAKE.

Chimps can not only be taught to communicate with specially designed computer symbols or sign language *(Nature/Science Annual 1975, Teaching Animals to Talk, pages 156-165),* but it now seems they also have special systems of their own that enable them to express complex ideas to one another. They can use barks and visual language—gestures, expressions, postures—to communicate information, reported psychologist Emil Menzel of the State University of New York at Stony Brook.

In a series of ingenious experiments, Menzel showed how details about food and danger were passed among groups of six or eight young wild animals that had lived together for at least a year. By then, they had acquired the habits typical of adolescent but not adult chimpanzees: They did everything as a cohesive group, and none would stray from the gang by more than a few yards.

In one test, Menzel locked the chimps in a small cage, then entered the large enclosure in which the cage was placed and randomly hid objects. One chimp was taken from the cage and shown the hiding places, then returned to its group. Minutes later, all the chimps were released from the cage.

If the object was close, the animal that had been shown the hiding place—"the leader"—immediately ran to it, followed by his companions. But if the object was farther away, the leader immediately began to organize its fellows. It communicated by a pointing motion of the head or hand, or by a few steps taken toward the hiding place. In some cases, complex information was conveyed. If the location of the object was not easily pointed out, the leader pinpointed it by triangulation; the animal would successively point to the hidden object from different spots, enabling all the followers to put the signals together and infer the exact location.

Menzel found that the leader could even indicate to its companions whether the hidden object was desirable or undesirable. When the object was a snake, for example, the leader froze a few yards short of it and barked in alarm. The rest of the group would then approach gingerly and some would probe or beat the area with sticks. But if the object was food, the leader would run right up to it and all the chimps would swarm over the designated area, exploring it confidently with their hands.

ANTS THAT RALLY THEIR TROOPS

Army ants live up to their name not only in their well-known habit of marching in dense columns, but also in the speed with which scouts mobilize soldiers for attacks on prey.

Writing in *Science* in June, Ruth Chadab and Carl Rettenmeyer, researchers at the University of Connecticut, described how a single forager can communicate instructions for a mass assault on a favorite food supply, the larvae in a wasp's nest. After spotting the nest, the scout heads back to the main column, leaving a telltale chemical trail on the ground as it goes. On arrival it rushes backward and forward among its fellows, touching their antennae and bodies to tell them what awaits.

The two scientists, working in the jungles of Ecuador, made their observations after lowering wasp nests into the path of oncoming army ant columns, whose vanguard of foragers first attacked, then returned to the main column. Within a minute each forager had recruited as many as 100 ants, which would then follow the trail to the nest. Apparently such blitzkrieg tactics are vital to the ants, for wasps can throw off attacks by small numbers but will abandon their nests when confronted by a mass assault, leaving the young behind to be devoured.

HORMONES FROM PLANTS

For more than a century it has been known that plants need insects as intermediaries in their breeding process. Now scientists have found some insects need plants for a similar purpose.

In November a team of chemical ecologists at Pennsylvania State University reported that a female insect's hormonal sex lure, or pheromone *(Nature/Science Annual 1972, Communicating by Smell, pages 89-95)* at one time believed to be produced in the body—is made by plants; the chemical is eaten by larvae and retained in adulthood by the female.

The team started on its quest when it began research to isolate the sex attractant of a pest called the oak leaf roller moth in the hope of eventually using it as a pest control. The scientists identified 17 chemical compounds in female leaf roller moths that, when placed in traps as bait, attracted males. But the researchers noticed something odd: Some males were also sexually attracted to the leaves of a nearby oak tree.

The scientists collected the leaves, ground them up, analyzed their chemical compounds—and found some that were identical to certain sex attractants of the female moths. When the team isolated similar pheromones from insects that feed on apples and mushrooms, they began to suspect that a wide variety of insects absorb sex lures from plants; this raises the hope that scientists can extract pheromones for pest control directly from vegetation. In addition, the work of the Pennsylvania team may explain a heretofore puzzling phenomenon—why some mammals such as deer and beaver are known to give off mate-attracting smells after eating certain plants.

FATAL FEMALE FIREFLIES

Fireflies mate at night, lured to the opposite sex by the periodic glowing of their abdomens. In fact, each of the many firefly species has its own distinctive mating signal, which differs from those of other species in the number, duration and frequency of the flashes. When female fireflies of the genus *Photuris* flash

their signals, however, they often have something other than sex in mind. By mimicking the signals of others, they are able to lure males of different species and then devour them.

This Machiavellian bit of strategy was discovered by James Lloyd, an entomologist at the University of Florida in Gainesville, who spent many nights signaling to fireflies with a pen light. He reported in *Science* that flashing the mating signal of a male *Photinus* would at times evoke the right response—but from a female *Photuris*. Switching to the signal of a different male species, he found the *Photuris* would mimic the proper response for the female of that species. All told, a female could imitate the responses of three species other than its own. The mimicry does not always work, but about one in every 10 males is taken in—and eaten—by the siren *Photuris*.

A FEMALE FIREFLY (LEFT) DINES ON A MALE.

THE WARM-BLOODED TUNA

The tuna is one of the ocean's oddities. While most fish have body temperatures only slightly higher than the surrounding water, the tuna is as much as 68° F. warmer, maintaining a body temperature much higher than that of humans. For years scientists have wondered why. Now zoologists at the University of Hawaii think they have found the answer.

In most fish the heat generated by muscular action is dissipated into the water as the blood passes through their gills. But the tuna, reported E. Don Stevens, How Man Lam and J. Kendall in August 1974, conserves its heat with a close-packed network of blood channels. The network, consisting of some 250,000 interlinked arteries and veins, acts as a miniature heat exchanger. The arteries carry cooler blood from the heart to the muscles, where it is used, warmed and pumped via capillaries into the veins to be returned to the heart. But the veins lie so close to the arteries that much of the heat is transferred, thus returning to the muscles before it ever reaches the gills. Since muscles work better when warm, this adaptation gives the tuna help in its hunt for prey.

ASTRONOMY

Studies of the farthest reaches of the universe indicate it is not only expanding but will go on doing so forever. From somewhat closer in comes the first detailed photograph of a star outside the solar system. And on earth, observatories around the world simultaneously reset their superaccurate atomic clocks.

THE INFINITE UNIVERSE

Ever since cosmologists agreed that the parts of the universe were born billions of years ago in a primordial "big bang" and have been hurtling apart ever since, they have been perplexed by the logical next question: Will the universe continue to expand forever? Or will the gravitational pull of each object on all the others decelerate the outward rush, pull the galaxies back until they crash together and perhaps set off another big bang in a never-ending cycle of birth and death. The question was answered in December by two California astronomers working independently. Their reluctant conclusion: The expansion will continue forever —the universe is infinite.

Hale Observatories' astronomer Allan

Sandage—after 15 years of painstaking measurements of the distances of nearby galaxies and the characteristics of their light—determined that the rate of deceleration of the outrushing galaxies was lower than the amount needed to halt the outward flight. He estimated that the universe had been expanding for 16 billion years—far longer than previously had been thought—and predicted that it would never stop.

Astronomer James Gunn, of the California Institute of Technology in Pasadena, used different evidence. He examined the movements and the brightness of galaxies to determine their approximate mass. He also estimated the probable incidence of "black holes,"—extremely small but concentrated remnants of stars that are invisible to astronomers —and the amount of dust and other matter in interstellar space. From these and other clues, he concluded that the universe has no more than one tenth the mass needed to pull it back together.

Both astronomers were perplexed by the notion of an "open," infinitely expanding universe. Said Sandage, who for years was a leading proponent of a universe that would eventually close in on itself: "It's a terrible surprise."

NEW LOOK AT BETELGEUSE

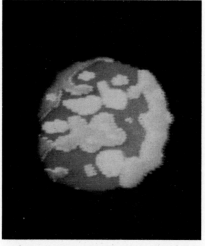

CLOSEUP SHOWS A DISTANT STAR'S HOT SPOTS.

Astronomers at Kitt Peak National Observatory announced in December 1975 that they had produced the first pictures

that captured the surface detail of a star. Previously, a photographic image taken through even the largest telescope was smeared into a uniform blob by movements in the atmosphere during the long exposure of the plate. But the Kitt Peak picture that was taken of the red giant Betelgeuse showed markings that scientists think may be hot spots in its atmosphere, perhaps from gases erupting violently from the interior.

To produce the remarkable picture, astronomers Roger Lynds, Jack Harvey and Peter Worden took some 40 photographs of the star through the Kitt Peak 158-inch reflector, the world's second largest telescope (twin to the one at Cerro Tololo *pages 104-107*), exposing each plate for less than a hundredth of a second. Each exposure, extremely short by astronomical standards, produced a circle of from 100 to 500 separate spots. This was the result of turbulence in the atmosphere, which broke up the incoming light, dividing the telescope's mirror into numerous smaller lenses. Each spot was thus a sharp image of the star, containing information slightly different from that of the others. Computer analysis of differences of light intensity from spot to spot provided the final picture.

RESETTING ATOMIC CLOCKS

At precisely midnight on December 31, 1974, time in effect came to a stop—for one second—at observatories located around the world as timekeepers inserted a "leap second" into the calendar. The corrections were made to keep the atomic clocks—which set the standard of time for the instruments of scientists and the watches of ordinary citizens— in step with one another and with the earth's rotation.

The correction was necessary because the earth's spin is being slowed rather erratically by friction from tides. The slowing rotation lengthens the day (one complete revolution of the earth on its axis) and thus the hour and minute. The more reliable atomic clocks begin to run ahead of earth time and have to be set back. December's correction was the fourth since scientists introduced the leap second in 1972.

DRUGS

From drug researchers came more bad news than good: Alcohol, tobacco and tranquilizers may have ill effects on the offspring of parents who had taken these drugs. And aspirin, the standard remedy for the common cold, may help spread the cold germs. The good news was only sort of good: a chemical test to forewarn potential alcoholics of their tendencies and the finding that it is never too late to give up smoking—ex-smokers suffer fewer heart attacks than those who do not kick the habit.

ANOTHER INDICTMENT OF SMOKING

Cigarettes, which have been accused of giving smokers everything from gum disease to cancer, have now been blamed for pneumonia and bronchitis in young children whose parents smoke. This dismaying conclusion was reached by Dr. J. R. T. Colley, of the London School of Hygiene and Tropical Medicine, and his colleagues after a study of 2,205 children and their parents.

The researchers interviewed parents within two weeks after the birth of a baby and recorded their smoking habits and any respiratory problems. The families were then approached annually for the next five years; they were asked to fill out questionnaires about their smoking and health and to report any instances of bronchitis or of pneumonia in their infants. The results indicated that the children of parents who smoked had bronchitis or pneumonia during their first year of life twice as often as did offspring of nonsmokers.

LESS RISK FOR EX-SMOKERS

The facts that helped link cigarette smoking to heart disease came from the Framingham Study, which since 1956 has kept watch on the health of more than 5,000 residents of Framingham, Massachusetts. The study has continued to pay dividends. Follow-up examinations of the 2,336 men in the group have indicated that men under 65 who give up smoking suffer fewer heart attacks and live longer than those who continue to smoke.

The new data showed that the rate of coronary heart disease dropped off almost immediately to about half that of smokers. The mortality rate for quitters also fell, but more gradually and to only three quarters that of smokers. It was concluded that "smoking has a noncumulative, transient, reversible triggering effect rather than a direct influence" on hardening of the arteries.

DRINKING LINKED TO FETAL DAMAGE

Can excessive drinking by a man lead to genetic defects in his offspring? That possibility was raised in a report on animal studies conducted at the Worcester (Massachusetts) Foundation for Experimental Biology.

A husband-and-wife team, F. M. Badr and Ragaa Badr, gave each of eight male mice alcohol equivalent to four drinks for humans, repeating the process for three consecutive days. Each mouse was then mated to a different female mouse each week for six consecutive weeks, and the resulting litters were compared to those from a nonalcoholic control group. Some of the alcoholic mice litters were smaller—especially those resulting from matings that occurred 14 days after alcoholic consumption ended.

In a follow-up experiment the Badrs gave 19 mice alcohol and mated them to females at four-day intervals. In the mice that were mated with alcoholic males the number of dead fetuses was significantly higher than in a control group, especially in those that mated from nine to 13 days after alcohol was cut off. To the Badrs the experiments suggested that the prenatal deaths might have resulted from genetic mutations in the male sperm that were induced by alcohol.

NEW CLUES TO ALCOHOLISM

Something in the body makes alcoholics react more than other people to a drink, according to Dr. Charles Lieber of New York City's Bronx Veterans Administration Hospital. He reported that acetaldehyde, a breakdown product of alcohol, reaches higher levels in alcoholics than in others—even when both groups have the same level of alcohol in their blood.

Alcohol was injected into the bloodstreams of six volunteers suffering from chronic alcoholism and into five nonalcoholics. Simultaneous measurements of both alcohol and acetaldehyde in the bloodstreams of the volunteers were made during the next eight to 10 hours. The result: Acetaldehyde levels in the blood of the alcoholics reached a plateau that was 62 per cent higher than that of the normal subjects. The finding indicated it is acetaldehyde and not alcohol that may cause alcoholism and the degeneration of the liver, heart and brain tissue that often accompanies the problem.

If further experiments confirm the conclusion of the Bronx researchers, their work could lead to the development of drugs to prevent alcohol-induced illness like cirrhosis of the liver—and perhaps to methods of identifying potential alcoholics and preventing the disease itself.

CAN ASPIRIN SPREAD COLDS?

Aspirin is the standard remedy for the common cold. That familiar prescription may well be ill-advised. In March 1975 a team of University of Illinois doctors reported that the use of aspirin apparently helps spread the cold virus.

In two separate experiments the doctors gave 45 medical-student volunteers nose drops containing common cold viruses, which caused between 60 and 70 per cent of them to come down with the classic symptoms of a cold. Some of the subjects were then given aspirin, others a similar-looking capsule that contained no drug at all. While aspirin produced slight relief in those who took it, daily samplings showed that aspirin users produced the virus in their nasal drippings more often than did nonusers. Three days after being infected about 80 per cent of the aspirin users continued to excrete some virus from their noses, compared with only half of the nonusers.

The reason for the difference, the Illinois team suggested, may lie in aspirin's mode of action. The drug suppresses the travel of virus-fighting white cells to inflamed areas; that effect reduces discomfort, but it also may promote virus growth and prolong the infection.

Thus, the researchers concluded, aspirin helps spread the cold virus in two ways. By providing relief, it encourages cold sufferers to remain on the job or go out in public where more people will be exposed to them. At the same time, by allowing more rapid growth of the virus, it makes their nasal drippings more infectious, increasing the chance that their colds will be transmitted to others.

YELLOW LIGHT ON TRANQUILIZERS

While scientists on the West Coast were indicting Librium and some other popular tranquilizers as the possible cause of birth defects, the federal government, in an unrelated action, tightened up regulations for prescription sales of Librium and a number of similar drugs.

In December 1974, two researchers from the School of Public Health at the University of California at Berkeley, reported that the widely used tranquilizers, meprobamate (Miltown, Equanil) and chlordiazepoxide (Librium) cause birth defects. Their warning resulted from a study of more than 19,000 live births to groups of women who had been enrolled in the Kaiser-Permanente Medical Care Program in California. The researchers compared the incidence of birth defects in the offspring of four groups of women, all of whom suffered anxiety or tension. They found that women who had used either meprobamate or chlordiazepoxide during the first six weeks of pregnancy had four times as many babies with birth defects as the group that had used no drugs and twice as many as those women who used drugs other than the suspect tranquilizers.

The study also showed a higher incidence of stillbirth among women taking either of the two compounds. While no one type of birth defect was associated with chlordiazepoxide, five of eight of the affected children in the meprobamate group had congenital heart disease.

In June the Justice Department, the watchdog agency for dangerous drugs,

imposed controls on the tranquilizers Valium, Librium, Tranxene and Serax, and on the sedative Dalmane. The regulations limited sale of the drugs—formerly available indefinitely to patients—to five refills within a six-month period on a single prescription.

The controls are a result of tests showing the drugs can produce "physical and psychological dependency."

ENERGY

Gloomy reports from around the world made an already dismal energy situation seem worse. A comprehensive survey of mineral reserves showed that the world is running out of oil as well as many other essential minerals faster than anyone thought. New Zealand's volcanic-steam generating plant turned out to be a prodigious polluter. And high-tension power lines may be hazardous to health.

A MINED-OUT WORLD

Dwindling supplies of oil and minerals. A series of shocks as worldwide scarcities appear in one major resource after another. Unrealistic estimates of remaining energy reserves. Disruptive shortages "only a matter of a few years away."

These were some of the gloomy appraisals in a massive report, *Mineral Resources and the Environment,* which was released in February 1975 by the National Academy of Sciences.

Among the material resources that the academy included in a "threatened list" were asbestos, helium and mercury—essential industrial materials that have no known substitutes. Minerals already in short supply included copper, nickel, gold and tin. The report predicted that most of the world's oil would be exhausted in 50 years and that the huge Middle East reserves would be gone in 30 years. It estimated the United States oil reserves at 150 billion barrels, most of it still undiscovered; this amount was less than half an earlier estimate by the U.S. Geological Survey. The United States has ample coal reserves, however.

POWER-LINE POLLUTION

LIT LAMPS INDICATE POWER-LINE FORCE.

Very-high-voltage power lines—the new systems of 765,000 volts or more, twice the voltage of most transmission lines—may pose a little-recognized danger, not from the possibility of shock but from the electric force they create around humans, animals and plants along their rights of way. The presence of such electrostatic fields can be dramatically demonstrated by bringing an unconnected fluorescent bulb close to one of the very-high-voltage lines; it will light up *(above).* That these forces can cause biological harm was shown by Robert Becker and Andrew Marino of the Veterans Administration Hospital in Syracuse *(How to Grow a New Leg, pages 94-103).*

In October 1974, they testified before the New York Public Service Commission that rats exposed for 30 days to a powerful electric force, similar to one created by a 765,000-volt (765-kilovolt) power line, failed to gain weight and suffered alterations in blood protein level as well as in the average level of a substance that controls stress responses.

There are now some 1,200 miles of 765-kilovolt power lines in the United States; there are plans for 10,000 miles of them by 1990, and lines carrying as many as two million volts are on the drawing boards. The very high voltages save energy by reducing transmission losses, and have been used for some time in Russia—where their dangers are recognized, according to a report by Louise and Peyton Young.

A long-term study by Soviet doctors indicated health hazards for men who worked at substations serving 500- and 750-kilovolt power lines. It showed that long exposure resulted in "shattering the dynamic state of the central nervous system, heart and blood vessel system, and in changing the blood structure. Young men complained of reduced sexual potency." From such tests, the Soviets ruled that a 400-foot-wide strip of land beneath 765-kilovolt lines is hazardous.

ENVIRONMENT

Man's often self-defeating efforts to re-create his surroundings in ways beneficial to his needs led to new concern about the effects of chlorine in drinking water, to a dispute over the production of "clean" auto engines and to an attempt to slaughter millions of blackbirds.

NATURAL BUT DIRTY POWER

Geothermal power—the steam from natural volcanic heat—has long been the dream of environmentalists because it promised energy without depleting basic resources, generating pollution or hurting the landscape. This dream faded when Princeton's Robert Axtmann reported on a five-month study of New Zealand's Wairakei geothermal plant, which supplies 7 per cent of the country's power. It pollutes both air and water.

Wairakei produces 6.5 times as much waste heat and 5.5 times as much water vapor as an equivalent plant burning coal or oil. Its emissions have the rotten-egg smell of hydrogen sulfide and tarnish silverware in a village over a mile away. The nearby Waikato River, into which spent geothermal steam eventually discharges, has also become contaminated with carbon dioxide, mercury and arsenic, as well as hydrogen sulfide. Both the increased temperature of the river water and the dissolved carbon dioxide have apparently contributed to the increase in weeds in nearby Lake Aratiatia, and there have been two recent large kills of carp in the lake.

Axtmann noted that the plant was designed and built before environmental concerns became significant and that many of these problems might well be solved by reinjecting hot-water wastes into the ground, or by purifying steam and reclaiming from it potentially valuable chemicals. But as it now stands, the plant is a prodigious polluter—a fact that apparently has not been told to the tourist officer in the nearby Geothermal Information Center. One of the questions most frequently asked by the plant's 125,000 annual visitors is, "Are there any environmental effects?" Says the tourist officer: "No."

THE PERILS OF CHLORINE

Chlorine added to city water makes it safe to drink by killing disease bacteria. It may also make it somewhat less safe by increasing concentrations of worrisome chemicals. Two announcements raised concern over this protective measure, long relied on by most cities.

In November 1974 the federal Environmental Protection Agency revealed that highly active chlorine combines with impurities in water to produce such dangerous compounds as chloroform and carbon tetrachloride. Chloroform has been found to cause cancer in animals and carbon tet, a known poison, is a suspected cancer agent.

At the same time the Environmental Defense Fund published a study that —while limited and preliminary—indicated a "significant relationship" between the consumption of Mississippi River drinking water, which is chlorinated before use, and deaths resulting from cancers of the urinary organs and the gastrointestinal tract.

EPA Administrator Russell Train emphasized that while chlorination does produce some harmful compounds, it remained the best method of preventing bacterial diseases. "We continue to believe," he concluded, "that the benefits of chlorine used to prevent immediate, acute biological diseases far outweigh the potential health risks."

AUTO CATALYST BACKFIRE

The government admitted that it might have been wrong in pushing for the catalytic converter required on the exhaust

VOLCANIC STEAM FOR POWER, SUPPOSEDLY CLEAN, CLOUDS—AND POLLUTES—NEW ZEALAND.

systems of all 1975 cars to reduce emission of pollutants. Environmental Protection Agency Administrator Russell Train announced in March 1975 that tests had shown that the converters transform sulfur in the gasoline into minute quantities of sulfuric acid mist. In high enough concentrations the mist would be a health hazard, especially to people with respiratory problems.

Train asked Congress to delay requirements for a more advanced converter until the 1982-model year. That would give the auto makers time to produce a virtually pollution-free engine, and would eliminate the need for the converter. But General Motors, which had spent some $350 million on the device and had finally backed it with enthusiasm, joined environmental groups in urging the government to solve the sulfuric acid problem not by abandoning the converters but by removing sulfur from gasoline, either at the refineries or in the car.

Meanwhile, another possible hazard of catalytic converters was revealed when Gulf Oil Chemicals Company warned plant managers that the surface temperature of converters could climb from a normal 600° F. to 990° F. under severe conditions—when, for example, the car was climbing a hill at full throttle. "These temperatures were judged to be sufficient to ignite hydrocarbon vapors or to start grass fires," the warning said. Concerned about the possible fire hazard, eight oil refineries and chemical plants on the Texas coast banned automobiles equipped with converters from driving on their properties.

eral skirmishes: filing an environmental impact statement, warding off angry environmentalists and defeating court suits brought by two humane societies. Finally, on a chilly night in February 1975, Huey helicopters attacked, spraying the roosting birds with Tergitol-9, which is a detergent that can dissolve the oil on birds' feathers. Then fire trucks doused the birds with water, washing off the oil. Exposed to 40° F. weather without insulating oil, about a half million blackbirds died of the cold.

"I'm satisfied with the operation," stated Brigadier General John Brandenberg. "We had reasonably good success." But millions of the starlings, grackles, cowbirds and blackbirds had survived, probably to proliferate and return in even greater numbers the next fall.

WAR ON BLACKBIRDS

DOOMED BIRDS DARKEN KENTUCKY SKIES BEFORE AN EXTERMINATION CAMPAIGN BEGINS.

"This is a pestilence and a scourge," declared George Atkins, Mayor of Hopkinsville, Kentucky. "Farmers are in the fields with shotguns, cattle and hogs are driven from the feed lots, and children's slides are covered with bird droppings." Atkins was complaining about the five million starlings, cowbirds, grackles and blackbirds that had been roosting in a pine forest in nearby Fort Campbell since October, doing millions of dollars' worth of damage and making life miserable for everyone in the area.

The Army declared war on blackbirds. After fruitlessly playing recorded bird distress calls, setting off firecrackers and even thinning out the stand of trees, the Army announced a "blackbird control program" to destroy the pests. But the big push could not begin until after sev-

GEOLOGY

New understanding of the structure of the earth, arising from the continental-drift theory, paid off around the globe. In the United States geologists confirmed, as theory predicted, the existence of a subterranean current of molten rock. And in China scientists applied their knowledge to forecast—and prepare for—a severe earthquake.

AFTERMATH: FIERY SUNSETS

Beginning in October and November, areas ranging from Hawaii to France were treated to remarkably brilliant sunsets. The Western sky turned successively purple, ocher, yellow, orange and red, then brightened strangely a half hour after the sun had disappeared.

The source of these celestial spectaculars was Guatemala's Volcán de Fuego, which erupted in October, showering rocks on nearby villages, depositing ashes as far north as Mexico and throwing a huge cloud of dust into the atmosphere. The dust, by performing a variety of optical tricks with light from the descending sun, put on the evening show.

NASA physicists William Fuller Jr. and Michael McCormick, after surveying the stratosphere with lidar (a system that emits pulses of red laser light and records the light reflected back from the atmosphere), first found Fuego's cloud to consist of two layers at altitudes of 9.6 and 12.2 miles. By January, the layers had consolidated into a single one that reflected back about three and a half times the light of a dust-free stratosphere. Thus after sunset, sunlight—reddened by its passage through several hundred miles of atmosphere to the west —was reflecting off the dust layer, providing both the pyrotechnic display and the temporary brightening of the sky before nightfall. Scientists expected the fiery sunsets to persist for a year.

HOT SPOTS IN YELLOWSTONE

Most geologists now believe the earth's surface consists of huge shifting plates that make continents drift, build mountains, open deep-sea trenches and bring about other phenomena that until a decade ago had never been satisfactorily explained. But what makes the plates move? One popular hypothesis is that there are some 20 thermal plumes—columns of magma (molten rock, hot liquid and gases) a few hundred kilometers in diameter—that rise from deep in the earth's hot mantle and spread under the giant plates, shifting them around. At a December meeting of the American Geophysical Union, H. M. Iyer of the U.S. Geological Survey presented what seemed to be the first direct evidence for the existence of such a plume—under Yellowstone National Park.

Yellowstone is famous for its geysers, hot springs and other thermal activity, known to be caused by a body of magma under the park. Because Yellowstone is also the site of many minor earthquakes, the U.S. Geological Survey in 1963 set up seismographs to monitor the tremors. These instruments also detected shock waves from distant quakes, and by plotting their paths Iyer and his associates were able for the first time to estimate the shape and dimensions of Yellowstone's magma. It is pear shaped, some 50 kilometers wide at the middle and at least 150 kilometers deep. Iyer reported that more seismographs were being set up to measure the depth of the magma under Yellowstone, and perhaps to verify the existence of a long-sought thermal plume.

CHINA'S EARTHQUAKE ALARM

Although many scientists believe earthquakes can now be forecast accurately enough to get people out of harm's way when a severe quake threatens a populated area, no warning system has yet been set up—except in China. The first hint of the scheme's effectiveness involved the tremor of February 4, 1975. It was recorded by seismographs at 7.3 on the Richter scale—a quake of extreme severity—and pinpointed in densely populated Liaoning Province.

The People's Republic of China is notoriously tight-lipped about disasters, but Hong Kong newsmen reported that messages of condolence had been sent to Peking from leaders of Eastern bloc countries. Then a few weeks later a Chinese broadcast monitored by the CIA stated authorities had "mobilized the masses" before the disaster. The action was "based on earthquake forecasts and notices issued by our country's earthquake stations and posts." As a result, the broadcast claimed, "injuries were reduced to a minimum."

The Chinese are known to have a network of earthquake stations manned by 10,000 professionals. If they indeed performed as Peking claimed, it marked the first time that a major quake has been predicted and a population warned in time to take precautionary measures.

HOW THE ICE AGES BEGAN

The great ice ages that began approximately two million years ago might have been caused by worldwide volcanic activity, claim oceanographers James Kennett and Robert Thunell of the University of Rhode Island. They base their theory on core samples of ocean sediments brought up by the deep-drilling ship Glomar Challenger.

At levels of the cores that were laid down about two million years ago, the scientists found substantial layers of volcanic ash, indicating that there had been widespread volcanic activity at the time. They reasoned that the eruptions had pumped so much dust into the atmosphere that a substantial part of the sun's radiation had been blocked, resulting in lower temperatures—just as dust from the eruption of Krakatoa in Indonesia in 1883 caused cooler weather for several years in many parts of the world.

But the Rhode Island scientists also acknowledged that the cause and effect might have been reversed—that volcanism might well have been stirred up by rapid variations in climate. As temperatures dropped, more and more water was absorbed by the ice caps; the volume of ocean water decreased, lessening the load on the ocean basins. If warming temperatures then increased the ocean volume, placing a greater load on the basins, the changes in loading could have caused large-scale movements in the earth's mantle, which in turn may have triggered the volcanism.

MEDICINE

The many medical advances made in 1975 included discovery of possible new causes for cancer and two imaginative heart operations—one to seal holes in the heart with miniature "umbrellas" and another to back up an ailing heart by implanting a second one.

INSTALLING A SPARE HEART

In November, nearly seven years after he performed the first human heart transplant, South African surgeon Christiaan Barnard again made medical history. He gave a man not a new heart, but an extra one. In a five-hour operation, Dr. Barnard implanted the heart of a 10-year-old child, who was the victim of an automobile accident, in the chest of the Ivan Taylor, 58, leaving most of Taylor's old heart in place.

Taylor died four months after the operation, not because the body had rejected its second heart but because a blood clot had traveled up a vein to his lung, killing him instantly.

Barnard's next patient fared better. The doctor placed a second heart in a 47-year-old man who had had an artificial valve in his own heart since 1968. Some three and a half months after the operation, the man's new heart was continuing to beat strongly and the patient was able to resume a normal life.

PATCHING A HEART FROM OUTSIDE

A simple method that might eliminate the need for the expensive and still risky procedures of open-heart surgery was successfully demonstrated by Drs. Terry King and Noel Mills of New Orleans' Ochsner Foundation Hospital. They used the technique to patch a hole in the wall separating the two upper chambers of the heart of a 17-year-old girl. The operation took 90 minutes, and the girl left the hospital nine days later.

The two physicians made a small incision in the patient's right thigh, inserted a fine tube, and worked it through a pathway of veins into her heart and through the hole in the heart-chamber wall. At the end of the tube was a small capsule containing two folded umbrella-like patches made of plastic and steel. With a wire through the tube, the doctors extended the first umbrella and pulled it back against the edges of the hole. Then, on the other side of the opening, the second umbrella was opened and clamped to the first, sealing the hole.

SOUND MIRAGES OF THE DEAF

An 83-year-old woman who had been deaf for 25 years had trouble falling asleep because she kept hearing a medley of Irish jigs and Christmas carols. A 75-year-old man who had been deaf for more than a decade was so annoyed by voices singing familiar hymns that he often turned on a radio in an attempt to drown out the noise. Both these elderly people thought they were going crazy. In fact, they were victims of a deafness side effect that has gone largely unnoticed

and is frequently wrongly diagnosed: auditory hallucinations that, like the "phantom limb" sensations of amputees, are of physiological, not psychiatric origin.

In a February report, five Boston specialists cautioned other doctors against mistakenly sending victims of these hallucinations to psychiatrists. The hallucinations, which usually begin after a long interval of progressive hearing loss, are generally blamed on brain damage or on psychosis; few physicians know about the physiological source of the hallucinations because only five substantiated cases have been reported in English-language medical journals. The number of these cases may be considerably higher, the report said, because "patients may be reluctant to mention the symptom for fear that it would suggest a psychiatric disorder."

ATOM SMASHERS FOR CANCER

During the poverty-stricken 1930s, physicists raised money for their atom smashers by promising that these machines would provide better ways to treat cancer. That promise has been fulfilled only partially—until now. In March 1975 radiologists revealed that a product of atom smashers—a subatomic particle called the pion—should be safer and more efficient than X-rays at destroying some kinds of localized cancers and may be used as a means of treating patients as early as 1976.

Pions, which are subatomic particles embodying the force that holds together the rest of the structure in the nucleus of an atom, are capable of passing through living tissue without causing any significant damage. However, when they stop, they are captured by the atomic nuclei inside nearby cells. The nuclei then explode, showering the cells with fragments and thus destroying them.

That phenomenon makes the pion ideal for reaching and destroying localized cancers without harming the surrounding healthy tissue. Scientists can control the depth of tissue that the pions will penetrate before stopping, by varying the energy, or speed, of the particles. Thus they can cause a beam of the pions to stop in the tumor area, destroying only

the cancerous cells. According to Dr. Morton Kligerman, of the University of New Mexico Cancer Center, pion therapy is three times more effective than X-rays in killing tumor cells; it also destroys oxygen-deficient cancer cells that are ordinarily resistant to the standard kind of radiation treatment.

Development of pion therapy is already underway at Los Alamos Scientific Laboratory in New Mexico and at Stanford. The catch: cost. A pion therapy machine for hospital use would require five million dollars to build.

VACCINE FOR A CANCER VIRUS

Two West German researchers revealed in January that they had immunized monkeys against a virus that causes cancer in these animals. A killed-virus vaccine was used, which sharply reduces the chance that the vaccine may bring on the disease instead of preventing it.

For their experiments, Göttingen University's Rainer Laufs and Hans Steinke chose cotton-topped marmosets. These small South American monkeys develop lymphoma, a cancer of the lymphatic system, when they are exposed to either of two types of viruses. The scientists used a combination of heat and formaldehyde to kill cancer-causing saimiri viruses in a vaccine that they injected into 42 monkeys. Twenty-two of these marmosets and a control group of unvaccinated marmosets were then exposed to live saimiri viruses. Of the vaccinated monkeys, all remained healthy for periods as long as 337 days. The nonvaccinated animals did not fare as well; 12 out of 21 died of lymphomas within 52 days after exposure.

A CLASS PROJECT PAYS OFF

As part of a class project, University of California biochemist Bruce Ames asked his students to bring in various consumer products. His objective: to determine if any of the products caused genetic changes in a common bacteria called *Salmonella typhimurium*. All the products proved negative except one—a hair dye, which in Ames's words was "highly active." That finding concerned Ames. In previous work he had determined that about three quarters of the chemicals known to produce cancer also caused genetic changes in test bacteria.

Ames set about testing other hair dyes readily available to the 20 million Americans who use them, and in March 1975 announced the results of his careful experiments: 150 of the 169 hair dyes tested are mutagens—substances that cause changes in the genetic characteristics of the salmonella bacteria. In analyzing the dyes, Ames found that many of the chemicals they contain are closely related to substances that are known carcinogens (cancer producers). He concluded that "each of the hair dye compounds we have found to be mutagenic has a high probability of proving to be a carcinogen." Because the chemicals could damage genetic material, he warned, they might also increase the risk of human birth defects.

Animal tests of hair dyes have not yet been shown to produce either genetic changes or tumors, but the Food and Drug Administration announced that it had already begun testing the hair dyes that were the most active in Ames's tests.

NEW NCI REPORT RAISES QUESTIONS

One of the most massive studies ever undertaken by the National Cancer Institute confirmed what many doctors and environmentalists had suspected—a strong link between certain types of cancer and some kinds of industrial pollution.

Bladder cancer, for example, reached a significantly high level in 64 counties in the United States. Many of these were clustered in areas where automobile or heavy-machinery plants were located. Most others were in places—especially in the Northeast—where there were heavy concentrations of chemical plants. In New Jersey every county scored in the top 10 per cent of the nation for bladder cancer. Across the nation, lung cancer rates were high in the vicinity of copper and lead smelters. The researchers believed that the arsenic given off during refining was responsible.

But pollution was only one factor related to cancer that turned up. Some findings seemed logical, others strange:

• There was a significantly higher incidence of lung cancer along the Gulf Coast from New Orleans west to Houston, a phenomenon for which the NCI team had no ready explanation.
• Stomach cancer struck most heavily among people of Scandinavian and German descent in the Midwest. This suggested a genetic predisposition, since Scandinavians and Germans are generally more prone to stomach cancer than the average American.
• Cervical cancer was found most often in the Northeast and Appalachia, apparently among groups at the low end of the social order. Why social level should matter can only be guessed at.

EARS FORETELL DISEASE

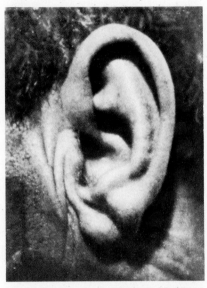

AN EAR CREASE HINTS OF DISEASE TENDENCY.

"When you examine a lot of hospital patients and you've got your stethoscope on a patient's chest," says Dr. Edgar Lichstein, "the first thing to come into view is the ear. It sticks right in your face." What Lichstein noticed about the ears is that those belonging to heart patients often had a distinctive, diagonal crease across their lobes. That observation led to a study by a team of doctors at New York City's Mount Sinai Hospital, who found that 47 per cent of patients who were hospitalized with heart attacks had creased ear lobes, compared with

only 30 per cent of patients admitted for other illnesses.

No one is certain what causes the crease—which often occurs without any corresponding evidence of coronary disease—but Lichstein reasoned that it is a skin manifestation of some inherited susceptibility to heart trouble.

AND NOW, HUMAN PHEROMONES

Scientists have known for years that virtually all animals secrete pheromones, aromatic chemicals that trigger specific behavior—often sexual—among other animals of the same species. Whether such substances are also produced by humans (Nature/Science Annual 1972, Communicating by Smell, pages 88-95) was until recently the subject of lively speculation among scientists and laymen alike. In December, a team of psychiatrists and researchers at the Emory School of Medicine and at Georgia Mental Health Institute, both in Atlanta, put an end to the speculation. They reported that they had succeeded in isolating from vaginal secretions of young women the same pheromones known to act as sexual attractants on male rhesus monkeys.

The concentration of pheromones in the secretions varied according to the menstrual cycle; the levels were highest during the middle of the cycle (the most fertile time) and lowest at the beginning of the cycle (the least fertile time). In women who used the pill—which prevents conception by altering hormone supplies—the concentration of pheromones remained about the same throughout the cycle, but was generally lower than among nonusers.

Psychiatrist Richard Michael, who directed the study, doubted that pheromones had much effect on human behavior. And if they did, he said, the American penchant for bathing and artificial scents would probably do much to negate that effect.

RESEARCH SCANDAL AT HARVARD

The paper published in two parts in the June and November issues of the Proceedings of the National Academy of

Sciences had been submitted by a group of Harvard University biochemists headed by David Dressler, one of the country's leading authorities on the body's immunity to disease. It had been judged and approved for publication by another well-known Harvard immunologist, Albert Coons, and had been sponsored by Nobel Prize winner James Watson, codiscoverer of the structure of DNA, the master molecule of heredity.

There seemed little reason to doubt the paper's significant claim: that the exact nature of the long-sought "transfer factor"—a substance that can be used to transfer immunity from one animal to another—had apparently been confirmed. But less than two months later, the validity of the paper was in serious doubt; Dressler had written a "statement of uncertainty and potential retraction" to a number of scientific journals, and the Harvard student responsible for it all had left school in disgrace.

The scandal began with Dressler's discovery that one of the undergraduates in his group, Steven Rosenfeld, 21, had written his own recommendation for a Harvard-M.I.T. medical program and had forged Dressler's signature at the bottom. Further investigation showed that Rosenfeld had also forged signatures to three other letters recommending himself for a fellowship as well as for election to the prestigious academic honor society, Phi Beta Kappa.

These deceptions immediately raised suspicion about the validity of the transfer factor experiments, which other scientists had been unable to duplicate, for Rosenfeld could have easily faked the results, just as William Summerlin faked his in the research scandal at Manhattan's Sloan-Kettering Institute *(Nature/ Science Annual 1975, page 172).*

After leaving Harvard, Rosenfeld issued a statement admitting that he was responsible for "several irrational, highly regrettable and unquestionably wrong acts," but he denied having tampered with any of the immunology experiments. "It would be tragic," said Rosenfeld, "if work were to stop on experiments in which we have invested so much time." But James Watson, for one, did not share Rosenfeld's view. "I think it's best to conclude," he said, "that the transfer factor doesn't exist."

AN OLD REMEDY REVIVED

A technique that keeps patients free of psoriasis—the itching, scaly patches of skin that afflict some 75 million people around the world—for a period as long as 10 months was announced in December by researchers working at Massachusetts General Hospital.

The new treatment for the incurable ailment, which is caused by abnormally rapid manufacture of skin cells, was inspired by a remedy popular among the ancient Egyptians. To treat a variety of skin diseases, they prescribed a powder extracted from a weed (the *Ammi majus* plant) that grew along the Nile. Then they exposed the affected areas of skin to sunlight. A similar procedure was used centuries ago in India. Contemporary researchers believe that the active ingredient of the powder used by the ancient doctors was methoxsalen, a drug that can be extracted from celery, carrots, parsnips and other plants and has been used since 1953 to treat another skin condition, vitiligo.

In the modern version of the treatment, patients with severe cases of psoriasis were given methoxsalen pills and two hours later—when the body's absorption of the drug had concentrated it in the skin—they were exposed for eight to 30 minutes to the invisible rays of a high-intensity ultraviolet lamp. The ultraviolet radiation apparently stimulated a reaction between the drug and the substances that regulate growth in the skin. The formation of new skin cells was slowed, and after a dozen or so treatments the patients were psoriasis-free. They also enjoyed an attractive side effect from the ultraviolet exposure: a deep sun tan.

METEOROLOGY

A satellite launched in 1975 will record broad "bulges" a few inches high in the ocean to help make predictions for shipping and weather forecasting. A spoof on the cause of tornadoes in the usually austere columns of Nature proved that suitably chosen statistics can be made to prove almost anything.

SATELLITE FOR THE OCEAN

Launched into an orbit that was nearly perfect some 500 miles above the earth in April, the Geodynamics Experimental Ocean Satellite has earned the accolade of being "the best-tracked spacecraft ever launched by the National Aeronautics and Space Administration." Its location, monitored by different systems, including laser beams, is known to within four inches. It has to be. GEOS-3 is meant to map the ever-changing topography of the ocean. Its radar altimeter bounces signals off the surface of the ocean and times the echoes, thus helping refine measurement of the "ocean geoid," the shape that the ocean's surface would assume without winds, currents and tides. The spacecraft will also monitor ocean swells and storms and will measure waves to within three feet of their actual height.

Data from GEOS-3 and even more accurate future GEOS satellites will someday be used in making regular "sea state" information available for shipping and weather forecasting.

TORNADOES LINKED TO DRIVING

In a tongue-in-cheek report to *Nature,* the prestigious British scientific journal, four University of California scientists added still another woe to the long list blamed on the automobile. Tornadoes, they said, were being stirred up by the two million cars and 600,000 trucks on highways throughout the United States, most of them in two streams of opposing traffic, each moving on the right. The twisting of air between these streams of vehicles, the scientists solemnly suggested, adds to the natural cyclonic spinning of the atmosphere in the Northern Hemisphere caused by the earth's rotation, and it is this increment that produces more tornadoes than would otherwise occur.

To support their joke, the scientists pulled off the kind of statistical sleight of hand that makes it easy to prove anything with figures: (1) Over the past 40 years, matching the increase in motor vehicles, there has been a sixfold increase in tornadoes. (2) In the last 13 years, the number of "wrong way" tornadoes (those spinning against the earth's rotation) has been quartered—presumably neutralized by the traffic-caused counterclockwise vortices. (3) Fewer tornadoes occur on weekends—when there is less traffic, most of it going one way. (4) There has been a gradual migration of tornado activity toward the East Coast, where traffic is heaviest.

The researchers offered a simple and practical solution for "vorticity pollution." If all United States vehicles were required to drive on the left, they said, "there might be an immediate and secular decrease in tornadoes, perhaps to levels below the natural intensity, duration and frequency."

NUTRITION

The often-changing advice of nutritionists changed again: Stop worrying about saccharin (it seems to be quite safe); try okra seeds (they offer very good food value); but do not take vitamin D pills (they may be too much of a good thing); and forget about vitamin C as a cold-preventive (it is no help).

NOURISHING GUMBO

Okra—its viscid green pods provide the distinctive ingredient in gumbo dishes—could become an important source of food protein if only the world's cooks would stop limiting themselves to using it green and would turn to its ripe seeds. Ripe okra seeds grow almost as big as lentils or soybeans, and are more nutritious, reported the University of Rhode Island's Spiros Constantinides to a Madrid meeting of the International Congress of Food Science and Technology. The seeds can be dried, pressed for oil and ground into flour, which could be substituted for about 10 per cent of the wheat flour used in baking bread. That would substantially raise the nutritional value of bread, he said, because of the okra seed's high content of both protein and the essential nutrient lysine. Lysine,

in turn, would help the body make more efficient use of the protein content in the wheat flour.

Although okra seeds are about 20 per cent protein, compared to 34 per cent in soybeans, for example, the okra plant is richer in calcium, iron, niacin and vitamin E. It also is capable of growing in poor soil and in regions that receive very little rainfall, where other crops that are high in protein cannot grow.

DOWNGRADING VITAMIN C

With his 1970 book, *Vitamin C and the Common Cold,* Nobel laureate Linus Pauling convinced millions of Americans —but few doctors—that large doses of vitamin C taken daily would prevent or cure colds. Three 1975 reports cast further doubt on Pauling's vitamin regimen.

Dr. Gerhard Schrauzer of the University of California at San Diego warned that large doses of vitamin C were self-defeating. Working with guinea pigs and then human volunteers, he found that large doses increase production of an enzyme that breaks down the vitamin and allows it to be flushed out of the body. If doses then are stopped, the body still excretes vitamin C for about three months, leading to a vitamin C deficiency.

In another study, 311 volunteers at the National Institutes of Health took a gram of either vitamin C or a sugar pill three times daily for nine months. When they seemed to be catching cold, the doses were doubled. The conclusion of the NIH researchers was that the effects of vitamin C on the number and severity of colds "seem to be nil."

Meanwhile, University of Chicago researchers found—after a review of studies of vitamin C conducted between 1939 and 1973—that there was little evidence of the vitamin's effectiveness in fighting colds. Some of the research indicated that large daily doses might even cause diarrhea or kidney stones.

A CURB ON VITAMIN D PILLS

Vitamin D is essential for normal bone growth and repair, and with that fact in

mind many Americans supplement their diets by taking vitamin D capsules. In December 1974, the National Research Council advised against this practice, warning that too much vitamin D could permanently damage the kidneys. The NRC action is an attempt to reduce the intake of vitamin D, which, beginning in the 1930s, was added to milk in a successful campaign to eliminate the bone-distorting ailment rickets, then common among children. Later, vitamin D was added to cereals and bread.

Reports that such fortification might produce an overdose first came from Europe, where fortification levels were higher than in the United States. Most people get enough vitamin D naturally from exposure to sunlight (skin cells make it) and from foods such as eggs and fish. With synthetically fortified cereals and milk—one quart contains an adult's full daily quota of the vitamin —there is almost no risk of a deficiency, and there is some risk of an excess if vitamin D capsules are taken in addition.

Because vitamin D promotes absorption of calcium from the intestine into the blood stream, too much of it can dangerously load the blood with calcium and cause the calcification of soft tissue. The addition of the vitamin to bread was stopped in 1973, and the NRC panel suggested that supplements should be discontinued except those prescribed for special reasons by physicians.

IS SACCHARIN SAFE?

After a two-and-one-half-year study, a committee of the National Academy of Sciences reported in January that it still could not say whether the widely used artificial sweetener saccharin produces cancer in test animals. The government thereupon stated that until conclusive tests were conducted, saccharin could remain on the market.

The NAS committee had reviewed the tests made by the Wisconsin Alumni Research Foundation, the Canadian government, and the U.S. Food and Drug Administration, all of which found that heavy doses of saccharin were able to cause tumors in the bladders of test animals. The committee also reviewed eight other tests that produced negative results, and criticized the Wisconsin and FDA studies, pointing out that impurities in the commercial-grade saccharin used for the tests—or factors not connected with saccharin—might have been responsible for the tumors.

The NAS team also found fault with several of the tests that had apparently exonerated saccharin. Noting that saccharin has been in use as a sugar substitute for 80 years with no evidence that it has caused any damage to human beings, the committee nonetheless cautioned that "this does not constitute ultimate proof of its safety."

PHYSICS

Research into an extreme form of matter revealed a strange new phenomenon: a "drop" of electricity.

DROPS OF ELECTRICITY

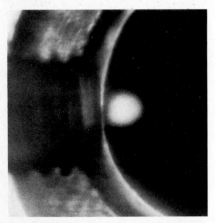

THIS GLOWING DROP IS "LIQUID ELECTRICITY."

In May scientists at the University of California at Berkeley announced that they had obtained the first photographic evidence of the most recently discovered state of matter—a bizarre form of electricity that resembles a drop of water. The drop (the bright spot at center in the photograph above) contains 10 thousand billion electrons—the minute, negatively charged particles that make up ordinary currents of electricity—togeth-

er with an equal number of positively charged "holes." A hole is the absence of an electron—a place in matter where an electron ought to be but is not; since that space should be negatively charged, the lack of negative charge makes it act like a positive charge.

Holes can move around in crystals as if they were positive particles (holes help explain why transistors work), and they can match up with electrons to form a bit of matter, called an exciton, neutral in charge because its negative electrons are balanced by positive holes. Excitons form only at extremely low temperatures, within a few degrees of absolute zero (-459.69°F.), the point at which all molecular motion ceases; at higher temperatures the excitons break up into individual electrons and holes.

Holes and excitons were useful theoretical concepts, but they seemed to be sort of convenient mathematical fictions until 1968, when Soviet physicists discovered that excitons actually existed, because they could be detected as larger "drops." Exciton drops do not exist by themselves, but only inside the spaces of crystalline matter. In that environment the electrical drop acts like ordinary matter, flowing around inside the crystal the way a water droplet would flow. It even has a surface tension similar to that holding a drop of water together; it boils when heated, turning to a gas the way water turns to steam; and if it could be cooled still closer to absolute zero, it would turn into a solid.

Soviet scientists discovered exciton drops by shining a laser beam on a chilled crystal of germanium (the transistor material). The laser energy excited germanium atoms so that enough electrons and holes were set free to recombine as drops. But these drops were extremely small, too tiny to be seen, although they were detectable by their electrical effects.

The Berkeley scientists found that by applying mechanical pressure to a germanium crystal they could cause tiny droplets of excitons to condense into a single drop 1/30 inch in diameter—several hundred times larger than the particles detected by the Soviets. Even though the exciton drop remained inside the crystal, its image could be picked up because an exciton emits infrared waves,

which were detected by a special TV camera, magnified and photographed. The technique is of great importance because for the first time it gives scientists a way to construct a visual model of liquid electricity.

SPACE

A dramatic beginning in space cooperation, the first joint venture between the United States and Russia, pointed to more productive exploration in the future. Of more immediate value were details about the solar system provided by the efficient performances of a lunar detector and two interplanetary probes.

A FINAL PASS AT MERCURY

In eternal orbit around the sun, Mariner 10 made its third and closest flyby of Mercury in March, passing within 200 miles of the planet's surface. It transmitted 1,000 detailed pictures and refined measurements of the planet's mass and location. It may also have upset a theory about planetary magnetic fields.

On its first flyby a year earlier *(Nature/Science Annual 1975, pages 154-155),* Mariner had detected a weak magnetic field that many scientists believed was generated by the interaction of charged particles, streaming from the sun, with the planet's surface. But data gathered during the most recent pass confirmed that Mercury has an intrinsic magnetic field that is somehow generated within the planet; its strength is hardly more than a hundredth as great as the Earth's.

That unexpected finding will result in some rethinking about the source of a planetary magnetic field. Scientists have assumed that the terrestrial magnetic field is generated within the Earth's liquid interior by a dynamo-like motion caused by the planet's rotation. Whether Mercury has a liquid core is uncertain. But even if it does, the planet rotates too slowly (once every 58⅔ Earth days) for the dynamo effect to occur. No further clues to the mystery can be expected from Mariner 10. Out of fuel and no longer maneuverable, it will miss Mercury by several million miles on its next pass.

THE LATEST FROM PIONEER

Swooping down toward the planet Jupiter on December 2, 1974, the tiny spacecraft Pioneer 11 seemed to go haywire. Sparks flashed, instruments performed uncommanded operations, heaters were turned on and the antenna feed unaccountably switched directions. The cause of the mischief was Pioneer 11's encounter with the most intense part of Jupiter's radiation belt, which bombarded the craft and its complex systems with charged atomic particles. But the spacecraft emerged practically unscathed, having swept to within 26,000 miles of the Jovian cloud tops at a speed of 107,000 miles per hour, and then having been whipped by the giant planet's gravity off onto a new trajectory that will carry it past Saturn in September 1979.

As it flew past Jupiter, Pioneer took the first pictures of the planet's polar regions. A year earlier Pioneer 10 had photographed the equatorial area (Nature/Science Annual 1975, pages 150-151). The new Pioneer 11 provided the clearest shots ever of the Great Red Spot (bottom, right) and Callisto, the second largest of Jupiter's 13 moons. Its instruments also measured the intensity of the radiation belts, and the strength and contours of the magnetic field. Some of the early conclusions from the mass of pictures and data transmitted back to earth:
• Cloud tops are lower at Jupiter's poles, giving scientists a chance to see farther down into the atmosphere.
• The wide white south tropical band that contains the Red Spot—and was photographed by Pioneer 10—appeared narrower during Pioneer 11's pass; its northern edge seemed to be breaking up.
• Jupiter's magnetic field—which pulsates like a "cosmic jellyfish" reaching out as far as nine million miles at times and then contracting to one quarter that size—may be produced by several electric currents spinning like generators deep within the planet.
• Callisto probably has a polar ice cap similar to the one on Mars.
• At the polar regions Jupiter's banded atmospheric structure breaks down into swirling scalloped forms spotted with storms that are probably similar to hurricanes (below). The turmoil occurs at the boundaries of opposite-flowing jet streams where wind velocity reaches 300 miles per hour.

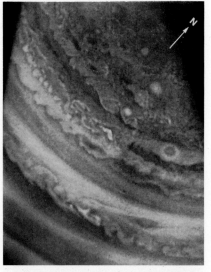

CLOUD PATTERNS BREAK UP AT JUPITER'S POLE.

JUPITER'S RED SPOT MAY BE A HURRICANE.

LUNAR ELECTRIC SUNSETS

When the unmanned Surveyor 5, 6 and 7 spacecraft landed on the moon during the 1960s, their TV cameras showed something that scientists had not expected on the airless moon: a sunset glow on the horizon. The glow seemed to indicate that the rays of the setting sun were diffracted by small particles suspended above the lunar surface. In April, NASA scientists finally explained this phenomenon. As the "terminator"—or day-night boundary—moves around the moon, small dust storms created by an unusual electric effect are stirred up along its entire length.

The scientists reported that a detector left on the moon by Apollo 17 astronauts had been struck by dust particles during the brief intervals when the terminator passed it every two weeks. The detector showed that at both dawn and dusk the particles were moving from the sunlit to the dark side of the boundary.

What levitated the moon dust and caused it to "blow" across the terminator? Scientists suggested that it might be an electric force generated between the sunlit surface, which is negatively charged because of ultraviolet bombardment from the sun, and the positively charged dark side. Negatively charged dust particles repulsed by the similarly charged sunlit side would rise as much as a foot above the surface and be attracted across the terminator to the positively charged dark side. As a result, observers watching sunrise or sunset from the lunar surface would briefly see the glow on the horizon as the sun's rays passed through the miniature dust storm.

The Apollo astronauts never witnessed the glow because their missions had to be carried out entirely in daylight.

AN INTERNATIONAL LUNCH IN SPACE

For what must be history's strangest lunch date, Soviet and American astronauts met just past noon on July 17, 1975, some 140 miles in space to share a meal including borscht, Russian bread, turkey and cranberry sauce—dehydrated or mashed, baby-food-style, in tubes. The much-heralded international linkup sounded like the Rotary Club. "Very, very happy to see you," said Colonel Aleksei Leonov, commander of Soyuz, in English, reaching to shake hands. "Ah, hello, very glad to see you," responded Brigadier General Thomas Stafford, Apollo's skipper, in Russian.

But this just-plain-folks atmosphere could not conceal the drama of a remarkable feat—watched on TV, as it took place, by millions not only in the United States but also in the Soviet Union. Soyuz blasted off from the Baikonur Cosmodrome in Kazakhstan early on July 15. Seven and a half hours later and some 10,000 miles away, Apollo—nearly twice as large—was launched. For two days the spaceships circled the earth, Soyuz as much as 80 miles farther out than Apollo, while orbits were adjusted. At 9 a.m., July 17, United States astronaut Vance D. Brand sighted Soyuz. Two hours later, Apollo overtook Soyuz, passed, made a half loop backward, and gently latched on.

The successful international mission climaxed three years of preparation. For one thing, each crew had to learn the other's language, to reduce the risk of misunderstood instructions. The Americans spoke Russian to the Russians; the Russians, English to the Americans. Even Stafford's Oklahoma-accented Russian, spoken very slowly with textbook word-choices, is easier for Russians to grasp than is fluent, rapid-fire English.

The major change in technology was the addition of a docking module and an alteration in atmosphere. Soyuz is designed for ordinary air—20 per cent oxygen, 80 per cent nitrogen—at sea-level pressure. Apollo is filled with pure oxygen at one third sea-level pressure. The difference was too great for quick readjustments, so the Soyuz atmosphere was enriched in oxygen and reduced in pressure. The changes required were so few, however, and the mission worked so smoothly, that hopes for international space exploration were strengthened.

TECHNOLOGY

Record breakers made the news: a proposal to build the world's largest airfreight carrier, a scheme to save the world's largest wooden airplane, sea trials for the world's largest troop ship and further plans for the world's most mysterious deep-sea "mining" vessel.

A WOODEN AIRPLANE RETIRES

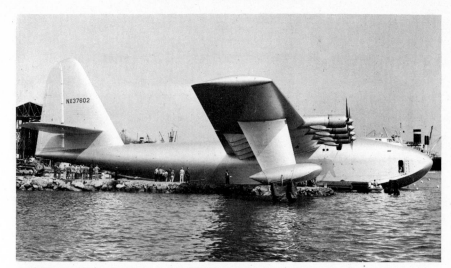

POISED FOR ITS ONLY FLIGHT, THE SPRUCE GOOSE FLOATS OUTSIDE ITS LONG BEACH HANGAR.

Howard Hughes's famous *Spruce Goose* is finally to leave the Long Beach, California, hangar where it has languished for close to three decades. In February the government announced that the wooden flying machine, with its gigantic 320-foot wingspan, had been sold back to Hughes's Summa Corporation, which would donate a 51-foot wing section to the Smithsonian Institution's Air and Space Museum in Washington, D.C., and make other parts of the plane available to eight other museums in other parts of the United States.

The craft, built toward the end of World War II, was constructed largely of wood (birch, poplar, spruce, maple and balsa) because of the wartime metal shortage. It was 220 feet long, had a wingspan of 320 feet and eight engines that could develop 280,000 horsepower.

It was designed to carry as many as 700 fully equipped soldiers as far as 3,500 miles at a speed of 175 miles per hour. But the airplane flew only once. On November 2, 1947, with Hughes manning the controls, *Spruce Goose* skimmed 70 feet above the waves in Long Beach harbor for about a mile and then was returned to its hangar for modifications, never to fly again.

Despite its inglorious performance, the *Spruce Goose* apparently captured the imagination of aviation buffs. News that it would be dismantled brought such widespread protests that, in April, Summa Corporation and the Smithsonian jointly announced that the dismemberment would be postponed for a year in order to give private groups time to raise money for putting the plane—intact—on permanent display.

NEW NAVAL TASK FORCE

The huge Navy vessel that began sea trials in the Gulf of Mexico during late summer is called an LHA for Landing Helicopter Assault, but it is more than an assault craft. It is a one-ship task force, capable of landing a 1,800-man armored battalion and its equipment.

Larger than all but the biggest United States aircraft carriers, the 39,300-ton ship can launch nine helicopters at a time and has an 820-foot flight deck for jet fighters. Within the LHA are one and a half acres of parking space, in which the armor and guns are stored until they are brought to the launching well on nine elevators, two conveyors and a monorail.

The LHA can also be used as a mercy ship, bringing supplies to disaster areas and serving as an emergency hospital; it has 300 beds and four operating rooms.

BALLOONS FOR AIR FREIGHT

When the French Ministry of Industry and Scientific Research asked ONERA, the French equivalent of the United States NASA, to investigate the problems of transporting great weights and bulky objects by some airborne method, it had every reason to expect a space-age proposal. Instead ONERA presented something that looks more reminiscent of Jules Verne's 19th Century fantasies.

Among the designs that the agency submitted was one for a dirigible-like, computer-controlled airship called the Obelix—named for a popular French cartoon character, a balloon-shaped strong-man named Obelix. It uses four huge balloons attached to a metallic frame for lifting power, and eight vertical and horizontal propeller engines for propulsion and maneuvering. Each Obelix would carry 500 tons and would cost more than $30 million apiece.

Despite the bizarre appearance of the ship and its substantial cost for design and development, which is estimated to be more than $200 million, the French government is taking ONERA's proposal seriously. Three of the big balloon weight haulers are expected to be in the air and working by 1976.

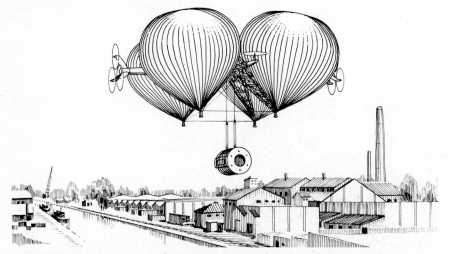

FOUR PROPELLER-DRIVEN BALLOONS TRANSPORT MACHINERY IN A SKETCH OF A FRENCH PLAN.

LASER-ENRICHED URANIUM

Scientists from the Los Alamos Scientific Laboratory revealed in April 1975 that they had developed a simple and relatively inexpensive laser technique for separating a specific isotope, or variety of atom, from material containing many isotopes of the same element. The announcement raised fears that technologically unsophisticated countries might soon have the capability of "enriching" uranium with uranium 235, the isotope required for atom bombs and power plants. That might well result in rapid proliferation of nuclear weapons.

The process involves the exposure of material containing the element to an infrared laser beam whose natural vibra-

tions match those of the atoms in the desired isotope. The beam excites vibrations within the isotope atoms, giving them sufficient energy to break away from the other isotopes in the element.

In experiments with sulfur, the Los Alamos group extracted the rare isotope sulfur 34 with an energy cost of only $1.20 per ounce—compared with the $30,000 per ounce by conventional separation methods. Physicist C. Paul Robinson, the leader of the group, said that the method, "if completely successful," could extract uranium 235 from natural uranium with only one hundredth to one thousandth the amount of energy required for present methods.

GLOMAR EXPLORER EXPOSED

The existence of the *Glomar Explorer* was never a secret. However, Howard Hughes's Summa Corporation—the apparent owner of the 618-foot ship—seemed unusually loath to publicize details about the *Explorer*, ostensibly designed to mine the ocean floor for nodules of copper, manganese and nickel *(Nature/Science Annual 1975, Mining Bonanza at Sea, pages 57-61)*.

In March the true—and fantastic—facts about the *Explorer* came to light. With its accompanying 324-foot covered barge, the Summa Corporation vessel had been built specifically to retrieve a Russian G-class submarine that had sunk to the bottom of the Pacific, northwest of Hawaii, in 1968. The *Explorer* in 1974 had in fact successfully salvaged part of the submarine from the ocean floor, some three miles below the surface.

What the *Explorer* actually recovered remained a partial mystery, compounded by a welter of conflicting CIA stories. However, one fact seemed clear: Some or all of the bodies of the sub's crew were retrieved and reburied at sea, in a ceremony filmed by CIA cameramen. There were reports that nuclear-tipped torpedoes or missiles had also been retrieved. Some sources insisted that most of the sub had been recovered. Others said the nuclear warheads and cryptographic devices still lay at the bottom of the Pacific and that *Explorer* was being readied again to salvage them.

TV SCREEN ON THE WALL

Electronic engineers have long dreamed of a flat television set that could be hung, like a picture, on the wall. This elusive dream came another step toward reality in December, when scientists at the Westinghouse Research Laboratories in Pittsburgh displayed the prototype of a flat-screen TV system that was only one eighth of an inch thick.

The new system depends on what may be the world's largest integrated circuit—a six-by-six-inch metallic chip containing the equivalent of tens of thousands of electronic components that form a graphlike pattern with 14,400 points of intersection. At each point, three circuit elements cause phosphorescent material above them to glow when they are triggered by a signal. Thus if a number of intersections are set off simultaneously, an image is formed.

In the prototype, the image was crude and had to be controlled by a bulky, external switching device. But engineers are working on integrated-circuit control devices to be imprinted onto the edges of the screen. A complete TV system might then fit in a picture frame.

WILDLIFE

While concern for rarities continued—grizzly bears, as well as several plants and insects, were added to the endangered lists—there were also encouraging developments. A lost gull demonstrated anew the adaptability of wildlife, and one nearly vanished tree, the chestnut, may be saved by a cure for blight.

SAVING INSECTS AND PLANTS

For the first time, insects and plants gained the dubious distinction of being called endangered species. In March 1975 the U.S. Department of the Interior placed 41 butterflies on its list of endangered and threatened species. And in January botanists warned Congress

MITCHELL'S SATYR, AN ENDANGERED INSECT.

that one tenth of the plants in the United States are imperiled.

The 41 butterfly types that are now legally protected against either capture or sale have been threatened by an upsurge in demand from collectors and by the destruction of their natural habitats as the cities and their suburbs expand into the countryside. Entomologists point out that butterflies are ecologically important because they pollinate flowers and provide an essential link in the animal food chain.

Scientists are equally concerned over the fate of plants. The first national inventory of native American plants uncovered the fact that 2,000 plant species are imperiled, mostly by the same factors that threaten insects: the activities of private and commercial collectors and the steady inroads of urbanization.

NEWLY PROTECTED: A PLANT, FRANKLINIA.

THE THREATENED GRIZZLY

CANDIDATE FOR THE PROTECTED LIST, A SCARCE GRIZZLY LOPES OVER A WYOMING FIELD.

Only a century ago an estimated 1.5 million huge grizzly bears roamed from northern Mexico to Kentucky to Alaska. Now, south of Canada, there are fewer than 1,000 of the giant beasts, most of them in three wilderness areas in Idaho, Wyoming and Montana. In an effort to prevent further depletion of the grizzly population by United States hunters, the Interior Department classified the animal a "threatened species." The category, which falls between "plentiful" and "endangered" and does not apply to Alaska where grizzlies are still plentiful *(Alaska pipeline, pages 64-65),* allows special protective measures to be imposed.

Neither conservationists nor hunters were satisfied with the new regulation. Lewis Regenstein, Vice President of the Fund for Animals, criticized the Interior officials for "formally endorsing large-scale hunting of an animal they admit is a threatened species—it's a mockery." Gary Abbey, a guide in Montana's Bob Marshall wilderness area—the only one where hunting will now be permitted outside Alaska—took a somewhat different view: "It seems to me that the regulations are unnecessary. I've been in the Bob Marshall since 1957 and I've only seen a couple. I wouldn't recommend coming here to hunt grizzlies anyway."

A REPRIEVE FOR THE CHESTNUT?

By fighting fungus with fungus, a new treatment may bring back the spreading chestnut tree, prized for its lumber, nuts and shade until a fungus-caused blight almost eliminated it from the American scene. The idea for the fungus attack on the blight stems from observations made by European scientists, who noticed that in some parts of the Continent, chestnut trees were little damaged by the blight. They found that these trees had been infested by a fungus less virulent than the normal type. Furthermore, in trees infect-

ed with both varieties, the more benign fungus seemed to transform the virulent one into a less dangerous form.

In February, Richard Jaynes of the Connecticut Agricultural Experiment Station in New Haven reported that he had injected both viral strains into sprouts from old chestnut roots to see if the virulent type could be tamed in American chestnuts too. It will be a year or two before Jaynes can assess the effect. But if the European fungus does blunt the attack of the native strain, it could be injected into the few remaining trees to keep the virulent strain under control and allow the chestnuts to recover.

THE GULL THAT GOT LOST

The resort town of Salisbury, Massachusetts, usually sleepy and desolate during the winter months, filled with visitors early in March. The unaccustomed influx consisted of dedicated bird watchers, drawn from as far away as Los Angeles to look at a Ross's gull, a rather unprepossessing sea gull that has seldom been found south of the Arctic Circle and has never before been sighted anywhere

in the United States outside of Alaska.

Only an experienced bird watcher would have noticed the gull that was lost. Among a flock of Bonaparte's gulls in the mudflats of Salisbury was a somewhat smaller gray-winged sea gull distinguished by a rosy chest marking, a wedge-shaped tail and red feet. Ornithologist Roger Tory Peterson took his eyes off the gull only long enough to spec-

ulate on how it had traveled so far south. After migrating from Siberia across the top of Alaska to the mouth of the Mackenzie River in Canada, the bird had somehow become separated from its own flock. It took up with a colony of Bonaparte's gulls in their summer breeding ground, flew south with them in the fall and now probably considers itself to be a full-blooded Bonaparte.

BIRDERS LINE UP TO FOCUS ON A NOVEL VISITOR: A LOST ROSS'S GULL (SKETCH, LEFT).

Credits

Sources for the illustrations in this book are shown below. Credits from left to right are separated by semicolons; from top to bottom by dashes.

Cover—Steve McCutcheon. 6, 7—Map by Nicholas Fasciano; Blair Pittman. 8 through 11—Blair Pittman. 12, 13—John Tveten—John Tveten; Blair Pittman. 14 through 17—Blair Pittman. 18—Henry Groskinsky. 20 —Map by Nicholas Fasciano. 21, 23—C. Donald Johanson. 24—Bobby Brown. 26—Drawing by Patricia J. Wynne; drawing by Susan Fox. 27 —Drawing by Susan Fox; drawing by Patricia J. Wynne. 31—C. Donald Johanson. 33—"Recueil de Planches sur les Sciences, les Arts Libéraux et les Arts Mécaniques," by Denis Diderot, Paris, 1762, courtesy *ARCHITECTURE plus.* 34—Wayne Thoms; Windworks. 35—Fritz Goro —Windworks (2). 36—Harald Glauth; Lisl. 37—Sandia Laboratories. 38, 39—Lisl; Robert Ferguson, Lockheed-California Company (2). 40, 41 —Drawing by Ed Valigursky. 42—Henry Groskinsky. 44—Gary Tannyan. 45—A. Lutzko, Prairie Regional Laboratory—K. N. Kao, Prairie Regional Laboratory (3). 47—Henry Groskinsky. 48, 49—Fritz Goro. 53 —Henry Groskinsky. 54, 55, 57—Jeff Foott from Bruce Coleman Inc. 58, 59—Ron Church. 61—Steve McCutcheon. 62—Drawings by Nicholas Fasciano. 63—Photo by Al Freni, inset drawings by Nicholas Fasciano. 64, 65—W. Ruth from Bruce Coleman Inc.—Steve McCutcheon —W. Ruth from Bruce Coleman Inc.; Jen & Des Bartlett from Bruce Coleman Inc. 66, 67—Don Carl Steffen; Steve McCutcheon. 68, 69 —Mark Godfrey from Magnum except bottom right Alyeska Pipeline Service Company. 70, 71—Mark Godfrey from Magnum except top right Doug Wilson from Black Star. 72, 73—Mark Godfrey from Magnum. 74—Lawrence Berkeley Laboratory. 76—Stanford Linear Accelerator Center. 77—Brookhaven National Laboratory. 81—European Organization for Nuclear Research. 83—Fermi National Accelerator Laboratory. 85—Lowell J. Georgia. 86, 87—Drawing by Dale Gustafson. 88, 89—U.S. Geological Survey, Astrogeological Studies Branch.

90, 91—Drawing by Dale Gustafson; Martin Marietta Corporation—Lowell J. Georgia; Jet Propulsion Laboratory. 92, 93—TRW Systems Group; drawings by Dale Gustafson. 94—Stephen Smith. 96, 97, 98—Dr. Robert Becker. 100, 101—Dr. Andrew Bassett. 102, 103—Henry Groskinsky. 105, 106, 107—Kitt Peak National Observatory. 108—Anglo-Australian Telescope Board—Anglo-Australian Observatory. 109—Anglo-Australian Observatory. 110, 111—Science Research Council. 112—Drawing by Nicholas Fasciano. 113—Drawings by Dale Gustafson. 114—Ken Kay. 116, 117—Drawings by Nicholas Fasciano. 118—Press Association. 121—Drawing by Nicholas Fasciano. 123—National Center for Atmospheric Research. 124—Harry Benson from TIME-LIFE Picture Agency. 126, 127—Lindsey Lampp, Baylor College of Medicine; Bob Simmons, Baylor College of Medicine; NASA. 128—Ohio Department of Transportation. 132—International Bureau of Weights & Measures; The British Library. 133—Schaefer & Seawell from Black Star. 135 —Musée des Techniques, C.N.A.M. 136, 137—Cartoon by Michael Ramus. 138 through 143—Derek Bayes from Aspect. 144, 145—Gail Rubin—Georg Gerster from Rapho-Photo Researchers; Liselotte Evenari. 146, 147—Gail Rubin. 148 through 151—Harry Redl from Black Star. 153—The International Synthetic Rubber Company Ltd. 154 —Ralph Crane from TIME-LIFE Picture Agency. 158, 159—Photo from Research Institute of Pharmaceutical Sciences, School of Pharmacy, University of Mississippi; both drawings from "Marihuana" by Lester Grinspoon. Copyright © 1969 by Scientific American Inc. All rights reserved. 160—Culver Pictures. 165—© David Scharf. 167—Drawing by Patricia J. Wynne. 168—Drawing by V. Puglisi. 169—Shelly Katz from TIME-LIFE Picture Agency. 170—Courtesy Emil Menzel. 171—James E. Lloyd. 172—Kitt Peak National Observatory. 174—Louise B. Young. 175 —Robert C. Axtmann. 176—Ken Murray for *The New York Times.* 179 —Courtesy Mayo Clinic. 182—J. P. Wolfe, W. L. Hansen, E. E. Haller, R. S. Markiewicz, C. Kittel, C. D. Jeffries. 183—NASA. 184—United Press International. 185—Drawing by Dale Gustafson. 186—Charles W. Mann from National Audubon Society—L. West from Bruce Coleman Inc.; Rod Allin from Bruce Coleman Inc. 187—Drawing by Guy Tudor; United Press International.

Acknowledgments

The editors are particularly indebted to Leon Jaroff, who wrote portions of this book. The editors also wish to thank the following persons and institutions for their assistance: Moid Uddin Ahmad, Professor of Hydrology, Ohio University, Athens; Earle Barnhart, Chief of Pure Energy Research, The New Alchemy Institute, Woods Hole, Massachusetts; Dr. C. Andrew L. Bassett, Professor of Orthopedic Surgery, College of Physicians and Surgeons, Columbia University, New York City; Dr. Robert Becker, Medical Investigator, Veterans Administration Hospital, Syracuse, New York; John Beers, Deputy Chief, Dimensional Technology, National Bureau of Standards, Washington, D.C.; Bernard Campbell, Professor of Anthropology, University of California, Los Angeles; Russell D. Cannon, Officer-in-Charge, Schmidt Telescope Unit, Siding Spring Observatory, New South Wales, Australia; Peter S. Carlson, Professor of Crop and Soil Science, Michigan State University, East Lansing; Thomas O. Chalk, American Wind Turbine Company, St. Cloud, Florida; R. R. Chelquest, Director, Division of Agriculture, Arizona State University, Tempe; Norman C. Cole, Master Optician, Optics Laboratory, Kitt Peak National Observatory, Tucson, Arizona; Paul Crutzen, Research Scientist, Upper Atmospheric Project, National Center for Atmospheric Research, Boulder, Colorado; Douglas Davis, Chemistry Department, University of Maryland, College Park; Robert F. Doolittle, Project Scientist, High Energy Astronomy Observatory Project Office, Systems Group of TRW Inc., Redondo Beach, California; Michael Evenari, Professor of Botany, The Hebrew University of Jerusalem, Israel; Kenneth L. Franklin, Astronomer, American Museum of Natural History-Hayden Planetarium, New York City; Robert Fridley, Professor of Animal Husbandry, University of California, Berkeley; Isaac Ghozeil, Supervisor of Optics Laboratory, Kitt Peak National Observatory, Tucson, Arizona; Philip Hahn, Chief Research Forester, Georgia Pacific Corporation, Springfield, Oregon; Clifton Hammond, Chief Engineer, Lockwood Corporation, Gering, Nebraska; Dr. Harold Harrison, Chief of Pediatrics, Baltimore City Hospital, Baltimore; Leroy Heidt, Support Scientist, Upper Atmospheric Project, National Center for Atmospheric Research, Boulder, Colorado; William E. Heronemus, Professor of Civil Engineering, University of Massachusetts, Amherst; David Hogg, Associate Director, National Radio Astronomy Observatory, Charlottesville, Virginia; F. Clark Howell, Professor of Anthropology, University of California, Berkeley; H. F. Hurlocker, Public Relations Representative, Lockheed-California Company, Burbank, California; Merle H. Jensen, Research Horticulturist, Environmental Research Laboratory, University of Arizona, Tucson; Clifford J. Jolly, Associate Professor of Anthropology, New York University, New York City; K. N. Kao, Associate Research Officer, Prairie Regional Laboratory, Saskatoon, Saskatchewan; Claud M. Kellett,

Project Officer, National Science Foundation, Washington, D.C.; Frank J. Kerr, Director of Astronomy Program, University of Maryland, College Park; Philip Krey, Environmental Scientist, Health Safety Laboratory, U.S. Energy Research and Development Association, New York City; Wann Langston, Research Scientist, Texas Memorial Museum, University of Texas, Austin; Douglas Lawson, Department of Paleontology, University of California, Berkeley; Randall C. Maydew, Manager of Aerodynamics Department, Sandia Laboratories, Albuquerque, New Mexico; Hans Meyer, Research Director, Windworks, Mukwonago, Wisconsin; Louis G. Nickell, W. R. Grace & Co., Columbia, Maryland; Walter Barry Nixon, Senior Technical Staff, Flight Research Laboratory, Princeton University, Princeton, New Jersey; Louis Perica, Director, Information Services, American National Metric Council, Washington, D.C.; Robert G. Petersen, Assistant Director, Division of Research, National Institute on Drug Abuse, Rockville, Maryland; Burton Richter, Professor of Physics, Stanford University, Stanford, California; F. Sherwood Rowland, Professor of Chemistry, University of California, Irvine; George D. Sands, Associate Viking Project Scientist, NASA Langley Research Center, Hampton, Virginia; Walter Schoenball, Managing Director, NOVA Energie Systéme, Geneva; Dr. Marcus Singer, Director, Anatomy Department, Case Western Reserve University, Cleveland, Ohio; Harold Smith, Senior Geneticist, Brookhaven National Laboratory, Upton, New York; Stephen Smith, Associate Professor of Anatomy, University of Kentucky, College of Medicine, Lexington; Gerald A. Soffen, Viking Project Scientist, NASA Langley Research Center, Hampton, Virginia; Ross Stein, Department of Geological Studies, Brown University, Providence, Rhode Island; Patrick Thaddeus, Institute for Space Studies, New York City; Samuel C. C. Ting, Professor of Physics, Massachusetts Institute of Technology, Cambridge; Donald J. Vargo, Technology Utilization Engineer, NASA Lewis Research Center, Cleveland, Ohio; Noel B. Vietmeyer, Professional Associate, Board on Science and Technology for International Development, National Academy of Sciences, Washington, D.C.; E. J. Wampler, Director, Anglo-Australian Observatory, New South Wales; Geraldine Watson, Silsbee, Texas; Steven Weinberg, Professor of Physics, Harvard University, Cambridge, Massachusetts; Victor Weisskopf, Professor Emeritus of Physics, Massachusetts Institute of Technology, Cambridge, Massachusetts; Richard M. West, Project Leader, European Southern Sky Survey, Centre Européen de Recherches Nucléaires, Geneva, Switzerland; George Whitfield, Department of Engineering and Cybernetics, University of Reading, England; Steven Wofsky, Professor of Atmospheric Sciences, Harvard University, Cambridge, Massachusetts; Mark Zahniser, Department of Chemistry, University of Pittsburgh, Pennsylvania; Israel Zelitch, Head of the Biochemistry Department, The Connecticut Agricultural Experiment Station, New Haven.

Index

Numerals in italics indicate an illustration of the subject mentioned.

PRINTED IN U.S.A.